Am I Hungry?
Mindful Eating Program

Companion Workbook
and Awareness Journal

for

EAT WHAT
YOU LOVE
LOVE WHAT
YOU EAT

Michelle May, M.D.

Am I Hungry?
PUBLISHING

Am I Hungry? Mindful Eating Program Companion Workbook and Awareness Journal, 7th edition

Published by Am I Hungry? Publishing
P.O. Box 93686
Phoenix, AZ 85070-3686

Copyright ©2010, updated 2018 Michelle May, M.D.

All rights reserved. No part of this publication may be reproduced, stored in a retrieval system, or transmitted in any form or by any means electronic, mechanical, photocopying, recording, or any other, except for brief quotations in printed reviews, without the prior written permission from the publisher.

Am I Hungry?® is a trademark of Am I Hungry?, P.L.L.C.

Visit www.AmIHungry.com for more resources.

ISBN 13 978-1-934076-34-7

IMPORTANT NOTICE: PLEASE READ

In view of the complex, individual nature of health and fitness issues, this book, and the ideas, programs, procedures, and suggestions are not intended to replace the advice of trained medical professionals. All matters regarding one's health require medical supervision.

The author's role is strictly educational in the context of this workshop and materials. The author is not providing any medical assessment, individualized therapeutic interventions or personal medical advice. Seek medical advice from your personal health care provider regarding your personal risks and benefits insofar as adopting the recommendations of this program.

The author disclaims any liability arising directly or indirectly from the use of this book or program.

Dedicated to all our workshop participants.
You've taught us so much!

Table of Contents

©MMXVIII, Am I Hungry?, P.L.L.C.

Table of Contents

 ## Welcome!

If you've struggled with yo-yo dieting, you're about to experience a whole new way of thinking about eating and physical activity. The Am I Hungry?® Mindful Eating Program will help you break free of your eat-repent-repeat cycle:

- You'll learn how to be in charge of your eating instead of feeling out of control.
- You'll learn how to eat the foods you love without guilt.
- You'll learn the truth about nutrition without confusing, arbitrary rules.
- You'll learn how to increase your physical activity and fitness joyfully.

How to Use this Workbook and Awareness Journal

This Workbook and Awareness Journal is the companion to *Eat What You Love, Love What You Eat: A Mindful Eating Program to Break Your Eat-Repent-Repeat Cycle*. The chapters covered in each workshop are listed on the first page, followed by summaries of the main concepts and questions to help you apply them to your own life.

Each workshop includes four important sections:

Think – This section is based on the Mindful Eating Cycle. It is all about how you make your decisions about eating. When you change the way you *think*, you change the way you *feel*, which changes the way you *act*, which changes your *results*.

Nourish – This section focuses on your food choices. Even if you already know a lot about nutrition, but this section clears up confusion *without* making foods bad or good.

Live – This section is about your activity; after all, one of the main reasons to eat is to fuel living. We'll talk about how to add physical activity to your life—and life to your physical activity. You'll learn how to increase your energy and movement, improve your health with exercise, and live a fulfilling life.

Awareness Journal – You can only change what you are aware of, so you'll record your observations about why, when, what, how, how much you eat, and where you invest your energy. As you capture *what* happened, you will better understand *why* it happened. (Tips: This is *not* a diet diary so no weighing or measuring needed! Take a flexible approach to journaling. Any time you write something down, you increase the information available to you for learning. Perfection is not possible—or necessary.)

More Tools

For additional support and resources, visit www.AmIHungry.com where you'll find mindful eating workshops, retreats, coaching, books, Motivational Companion Cards, Mindful Eating Virtual Coach App, the Mindful Eating Support Community, health and wellness professional training, and much more!

 ## Reading: Eat What You Love, Love What You Eat

Chapter 1   Think: Why Do I Eat?
Chapter 9   Nourish: Diets Don't Work
Chapter 17   Live: Born to Move

 ## My Workshop Notes:

 ## Think: Why Do I Eat?

Recognizing Your Eating Patterns

Rate the following statements on a scale of 1 to 10 with 1 = "I completely DISAGREE with this statement" and 10 = "I completely AGREE with this statement." Write your answers in column #1 after the first workshop and column #2 after the last workshop.

#1   #2

___ ___ I am hungry all the time.

___ ___ I am never hungry.

___ ___ I can't tell when I'm hungry.

___ ___ I know I'm not hungry but I eat anyway.

___ ___ I am starving by the time I eat, so I'll eat anything I can get my hands on.

___ ___ I eat by the clock.

___ ___ I think about food all of the time.

___ ___ I love food and eating too much to eat healthier.

___ ___ I think healthy food is boring.

___ ___ I use food to cope with stress and other feelings.

___ ___ I am an emotional eater.

___ ___ I eat when I'm bored.

___ ___ I eat when I'm stressed.

___ ___ I eat when I'm nervous.

___ ___ I eat when I'm sad.

___ ___ I eat when I'm angry.

___ ___ I eat when I'm lonely.

___ ___ I eat when I'm tired.

___ ___ I reward myself with food.

___ ___ I comfort myself by eating.

___ ___ I celebrate every special occasion or milestone by eating.

___ ___ I don't know why I eat.

___ ___ I often eat until I'm stuffed.

___ ___ I have trouble stopping myself when I eat "bad" foods.

___ ___ I have tried a lot of diets.

___ ___ I am either dieting or eating too much.

___ ___ I think thin people have more willpower than I do.

___ ___ I think thin people have better metabolisms than I do.

___ ___ I feel guilty about eating certain foods.

___ ___ I have a love-hate relationship with food.

___ ___ I sometimes ignore hunger in order to control my weight.

___ ___ I eat on a schedule even when I'm not hungry.

___ ___ I decide ahead of time what I'm going to eat for the entire day.

___ ___ I avoid certain foods because I think they are fattening.

___ ___ I am confused about what I should be eating.

___ ___ I am frustrated that the "experts" keep changing what we should eat.

___ ___ I hate to exercise.

___ ___ I don't really like exercise, but I do it so I can eat what I want.

___ ___ I make myself do more exercise if I've eaten too much.

___ ___ I dread the thought of going on another diet, but I don't know what else to do.

? Look over your ratings. The statements that you rated a 5 or higher are probably the issues that you'll need to work on throughout this program. Any insights?

Take this assessment again when you've completed this program so you can see what's changed. For a full report, take the online quiz: www.amihungry.com/quiz.

Hungry for Answers

? Describe someone you know who manages their eating effortlessly.

Instinctive Eating

Some people manage their eating effortlessly:

- They eat when they're hungry (they just know when their body needs food).
- They usually stop when they're satisfied (even if there's food left on their plate).
- They eat whatever they want (hopefully making healthy choices, but some do and some don't).
- They live an active lifestyle (this may or may not involve regular physical activity for optimal health).

We were all born with the ability to eat instinctively. To better understand instinctive eating, take a look at the Mindful Eating Cycle.

The Mindful Eating Cycle

The Mindful Eating Cycle is a way to understand the decisions you make about eating.

WHY? Why do I eat? This is the major underlying purpose or motivation driving your eating cycle at any given time. In other words, what is your "cycle driver"?

WHEN? When do I want to eat? When do you feel like eating? What causes an urge to eat?

WHAT? What do I eat? What food do you choose to eat from all the possible options?

HOW? How do I eat? How does food get from the plate or container into your body?

HOW MUCH? How much do I eat? How much fuel do you give your body?

WHERE? Where do I invest my energy? Once you've chosen and eaten food to fuel yourself, where do you invest that energy to care for your body, mind, heart, and spirit?

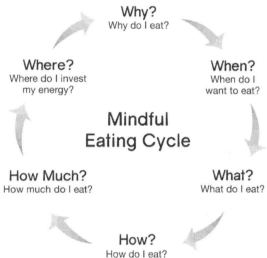

The Instinctive Eating Cycle

Let's apply the Mindful Eating Cycle to Instinctive Eating.

WHY? The main purpose for eating is to nourish and fuel your body.

WHEN? You eat when you notice the physical signs of hunger and the food you're hungry for is available. You just *know* you need to eat.

WHAT? You choose the food you're hungry for or what you think will be most satisfying from what's available. You eat what you love, though you may be conscious of nutrition and other factors when making your food choices.

HOW? You eat with the intention of satisfying hunger so you're likely to be attentive to your food. You're more likely to eat calmly, slowly, and without distraction.

Why?
Cycle Driver:
Fuel

Where?
Living my life

When?
When I'm hungry

Instinctive Eating Cycle

How Much?
Enough to satisfy hunger

What?
Whatever I choose

How?
Intentionally

HOW MUCH? You eat until you're comfortably satisfied; that may mean going back for seconds or leaving some on your plate, depending on how much you need.

WHERE? Your energy goes to work, play, and exercise. Your physical energy can be directed towards your activities; your emotional energy can be focused on your relationships and feelings; your intellectual energy can be focused on daily tasks and goals; your spiritual energy can be used for seeking peace, joy, and purpose. Once the fuel is depleted or stored, the symptoms of hunger develop, and the cycle repeats itself.

? Describe someone you know who struggles with food or overeating.

Overeating

People who struggle with eating:

- Often eat due to external and emotional triggers.
- Tend to be food focused.
- Eat to excess.
- May view exercise as punishment for overeating.

The Overeating Cycle

WHY? The cycle drivers are triggers that satisfy other needs besides the need for fuel. Eating provides *temporary* pleasure or distraction.

WHEN? You want to eat (or continue eating) when exposed to certain physical, environmental, and/or emotional triggers.

Examples of physical triggers other than hunger:

- Thirst
- Fatigue
- Pain

Examples of environmental triggers:

- Seeing or smelling food
- Seeing other people eating
- Advertising, cooking shows, recipes
- Time of day or year (mealtimes or holidays)
- Popcorn at the movies or doughnuts in the break room
- Food left on a plate, like a child's unfinished lunch

Why?
Cycle Driver: Triggers

When?
External or emotional cues

What?
Tempting or comfort foods

How?
Mindlessly, quickly or secretly

How Much?
Until food is gone or I'm uncomfortable

Where?
Excess fuel is stored

Overeating Cycle

Examples of emotional triggers:

- Stress
- Boredom
- Loneliness
- Anxiety
- Sadness
- Frustration
- Anger
- Even pleasurable emotions like celebration, love, and reward
- Other?

WHAT? What you want to eat is affected by *why* you want to eat.

? Write the foods you associate with each of the triggers above. Any insights?

HOW? How do you eat in an Overeating Cycle?

- Fast, "speed-eating." Leads to eating more but feeling less satisfied.
- Distracted, doing something else like working, watching TV, driving, or reading.
- Alone, in secret. This leads to guilt which drives the Overeating Cycle.

HOW MUCH? Since hunger didn't tell you to eat, how will you know when to stop?

- The food is gone, the plate is clean, or the bag or container is empty
- TV show, movie, or other activity is over
- Someone comes home or something else interrupts your eating
- Feeling miserably full, "stuffed," or physically sick
- Feeling numb

WHERE? Where does the energy go? Your body stores the extra fuel. You may feel more sluggish and be less active. Your true needs aren't met so the trigger returns.

? Now describe someone you know who always seems to be on a diet.

Restrictive Eating

When people try to manage their eating by restricting their diet:

- They are often preoccupied with food and/or their weight.
- They see food as good or bad.
- See themselves as good or bad depending on what they ate or how much they weigh.
- They may exercise rigidly to earn food or punish themselves for eating.

The Restrictive Eating Cycle

WHY? Your eating cycle is driven by the rules—the latest expert's rules or your own.

WHEN? The rules of your diet tell you when to eat (e.g. every three hours, 6 small meals per day, nothing after 7 pm).

WHAT? This is the main focus of most dieters. You eat what the rules of the current diet tell you to eat (i.e. no carbs, low fat etc.). This may be based on calories, grams, exchanges, points, or other methods of limiting your intake. The foods you allow yourself to

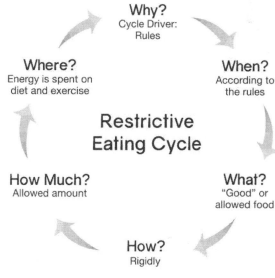

Why?
Cycle Driver:
Rules

Where?
Energy is spent on
diet and exercise

When?
According to
the rules

Restrictive
Eating Cycle

How Much?
Allowed amount

What?
"Good" or
allowed food

How?
Rigidly

eat may also be influenced by the scale or how well you followed your diet the day before.

How? Food is prepared and consumed in a controlled, rigid manner. You have to weigh, measure, and count your food, and write it down to keep track of what you eat (there's an app for that!).

How Much? This is determined by how much the rules allow, for example, one ounce of cheese, twelve grapes, or four grams of carbs.

Where? Sticking to a diet requires a lot of intellectual, emotional, and sometimes physical energy. Exercise may be used to earn the right to eat or pay penance for eating something "bad." People often exercise like they eat—rigidly. Further, if you significantly under-eat on a regular basis, your body attempts to conserve energy by lowering your metabolism.

The Eat Repent Repeat Cycle

The Restrictive Eating Cycle is not sustainable in real life for most people. Stressors, triggers, and hunger can overwhelm a dieter, leading to the end of the diet. When the diet ends, your exercise program often does too. Many people switch between the Restrictive and Overeating Cycles. When they're being "good" they feel deprived; when they're eating what they love, they feel guilty. We call this the eat-repent-repeat cycle, also known as yo-yo dieting. There may be days, months, or even years between cycles or you can switch back and forth within the same meal.

? Would you describe your eating cycle as mostly Overeating, Restrictive Eating, Instinctive Eating, or some combination? These questions will help you decide:

Why do you eat?

When do you feel like eating?

What do you eat?

How do you eat?

How much do you eat?

Where do you spend your energy?

? Do you struggle with yo-yo dieting—the eat-repent-repeat cycle? How does this affect your body, mind, heart, and spirit?

Learning to Eat Mindfully

In an Overeating Cycle, you feel *out of control*. In a Restrictive Eating Cycle you try to stay *in control*. Like a yo-yo, it is one extreme or the other; there's really no in-between because a yo-yo doesn't stop in the middle. The way to break this frustrating pattern is to learn to be *in charge*.

Instead of a yo-yo, think of a pendulum. As it gradually slows down, the extremes aren't as great and the arc gets smaller. The way to find the middle again is to use the Mindful Eating Cycle to guide you. As you discover a mindful way to make decisions, you'll have the freedom to eat what you love, the awareness to eat what your body needs, and the mindfulness to love what you eat.

? Describe in detail what your life will look like when you find the balance in between the extremes.

Nourish: Diets Don't Work

We live in a society obsessed with weight and dieting. Research has shown that size acceptance and learning to use hunger and fullness cues produces sustainable improvement in blood pressure, cholesterol levels, physical activity, self-esteem, and depression compared to dieting. Yet many people diet in response to societal pressure to attain an idealized body shape or size. Pursuing weight loss rather than well-being leads to attempts to lose weight regardless of the cost. Diets don't work long term for most people for many reasons:

- Diets consume a lot of time and energy.
- Diets cause deprivation, cravings, and guilt.
- Diets don't address the reasons people overeat in the first place.
- Diets ignore your own internal authority over when, what, and how much to eat.
- Diets are all or nothing. Life isn't.
- Diets may decrease your metabolism.

? Think about your past diets. How did you feel at the beginning? What happened over time? How do diets affect your thoughts, your relationships, and your activities? Why did you go off your diets? How did you feel then?

? Read "Don't Measure Your Self-Worth" in chapter 9 of Eat What You Love, Love What You Eat. What choices can you make to feel good now, no matter what you weigh?

Live: Born to Move

Movement is instinctive but modern society has developed ways to do almost everything more efficiently, automatically, and effortlessly. While these conveniences may save time, they also save energy—your energy, which may result in an imbalance. Even more significantly, less movement and a low level of physical activity may result in decreased fitness and well-being, so you may not have the stamina, flexibility, or strength to live your life to the fullest.

? Think about your lifestyle. Are you active or sedentary? Do you avoid doing things that require effort? Why or why not?

? Do you exercise to punish yourself for eating or to earn the right to eat? In the past, have you quit exercising when you quit dieting (yo-yo exercising)?

? Are you able to do all the things you'd like? Comfortably? If you were able to increase your physical activity and physical fitness, what would you do that you aren't able to do now?

Mastering Your Metabolism

Metabolism refers to the amount of fuel or energy (measured in calories) that your body burns each day. It includes:

Basal metabolism: The fuel your body burns to support basic, vital daily functions like your heart beat and breathing.

Activity: Everything from brushing your teeth to walking around your home or office.

Exercise: Exercise burns fuel while you're doing it and for a short time afterward. Additionally, exercise can increase or maintain

your muscle mass—important because a loss of muscle mass is a common result of dieting and decreased activity with aging.

? Do you think your metabolism is low, average, or high? Why?

? Describe your current lifestyle, including your daily activity and exercise patterns.

Boost Your Energy with Activity

You can start using your metabolism to your advantage by increasing your daily activity. There are so many ways to increase your physical activity, improve your physical fitness, and boost your metabolism! Be creative and mindful of opportunities.

? What specific things will you do to increase your physical activity in the following areas of your life? (Be specific!)

At leisure:

At home:

At work:

While out:

While traveling:

At rest:

 Action Plan

- Set aside 15-30 minutes each day for reading, journaling, and thinking about what you're learning. This is an important practice for this process—and for your life.
- Use your Awareness Journal to write down your observations and insights.
- Notice why you are eating and see if you can determine which eating cycle you're in at any given time.
- Notice when you feel like eating, what you feel like eating, how you eat, how much you eat, and where you spend your energy. What patterns, triggers, and cycle drivers do you recognize?
- Boost your metabolism by increasing your daily physical activity level.

 My Intention for the Week

Am I
Hungry?
Mindful Eating Program

Awareness Journal   Date_____

Time	Why?	When?	What?	How?	How much?	Where?	Notes

Mindful Moment

At what point will society begin to doubt the wisdom of diets rather than the fortitude of dieters?

©MMXVIII, Am I Hungry?, P.L.L.C.   www.AmIHungry.com

Awareness Journal

Date_____

Time	Why?	When?	What?	How?	How much?	Where?	Notes

Mindful Moment

Instead of following strict rules, become the expert on meeting your needs.

Awareness Journal

Date_____

Time	Why?	When?	What?	How?	How much?	Where?	Notes

Mindful Moment

When you're eating mindfully, you eat what you love, but you don't obsess about food because you don't need to. Instead, you trust your body to let you know when, what, and how much to eat.

Awareness Journal   Date _____

Time	Why?	When?	What?	How?	How much?	Where?	Notes

Mindful Moment

In the eat-repent-repeat cycle, when you eat what you want, you feel guilty; when you eat what you "should," you feel deprived. Either way, you're almost never at peace with your choices. Can you find the in-between?

Awareness Journal

Date _____

Time	Why?	When?	What?	How?	How much?	Where?	Notes

Mindful Moment

Instead of focusing on *what* and *how much* food to eat, the key is first understanding *why* you want to eat in the first place. This awareness will give you the opportunity to meet your true needs more effectively.

Awareness Journal

Date _____

Time	Why?	When?	What?	How?	How much?	Where?	Notes

Mindful Moment
A crucial step to breaking free of the eat-repent-repeat cycle is becoming aware of your thoughts, feelings, and actions—*without* judgment.

Am I
Hungry?
Mindful Eating Program

Awareness Journal

Date _____

Time	Why?	When?	What?	How?	How much?	Where?	Notes

Mindful Moment

Step by step, you'll learn a whole new way to manage your eating and build optimal well-being. You'll free yourself from your focus on food and discover new tools and energy to lead a more fulfilling, balanced life.

Reading: Eat What You Love, Love What You Eat

My Workshop Notes:

 ## Think: When Do I Want to Eat? Part I

The last workshop explored the *Why?* decision point in the Mindful Eating Cycle:

Eating Cycle	Why do I eat?	My insights:
Overeating	Responding to triggers	
Restrictive Eating	Following the "rules"	
Instinctive Eating	Meeting my need for fuel	

The next three workshops are focused on the "When?" decision point of the Mindful Eating Cycle to help you recognize when you want to eat so you can respond mindfully. When Do I Want to Eat? Part I helps you identify physical hunger cues and determine how hungry you are.

Am I Hungry?

Hunger is a basic survival mechanism. The purpose of hunger is to signal your brain that your body needs nourishment and energy. You were born with the ability to know when you need fuel. Many people who struggle with food are disconnected from their signals of hunger and satisfaction.

A remarkably simple but powerful way to become more aware of your body's cues is to **pause** and ask yourself, *Am I hungry?* whenever you want to eat. This deceptively simple question can be the answer to ending your struggle with food—*without* restrictive rules.

What Isn't Hunger?

The purpose of pausing to ask yourself, *Am I hungry?* before you eat is to help you distinguish an urge to eat caused by the physical need for food from an urge to eat caused by other triggers. We'll explore other triggers further in Workshops 3 and 4.

? What else, besides hunger, might cause you to want to eat?

? How can you tell when you're hungry? Write down all the symptoms you have when your body needs fuel.

Signs of Hunger
- Hunger pangs or gnawing
- Growling or rumbling
- Emptiness or hollow feeling
- Queasiness or nausea
- Irritability or crankiness ("hangry")
- Headache
- Low energy, weakness, fatigue
- Difficulty concentrating or making decisions
- Feeling you must eat as soon as possible

? What do these signs of hunger have in common?

Strategies: Body-Mind-Heart Scan

A Body-Mind-Heart Scan is a type of mindfulness meditation that helps you become fully present and aware of what's happening right now.

Pause. Move away from the food to allow you to focus and pay attention to what your body is telling you. Go to a "food-free" zone that you don't associate with eating. At a restaurant, determine whether you're hungry before you go inside. At a party or other social gathering, go outside or to the bathroom. If you can't

escape the food, close your eyes or turn away from it and focus inward for a moment. Take a few deep breaths to calm yourself.

Body: Focus on your physical sensations as you slowly scan from head to toe. Ask yourself, *How does my stomach feel?* Put your fist there or picture it as a balloon. Is it empty, full, or in-between? Notice other sensations. Are you light-headed, queasy, or irritable?

Mind: Focus on your thoughts since they may give you clues about whether or not you're hungry. Notice thoughts like *It's been a few hours since I ate* or *Mmmm, that looks delicious – and it's free!* Remember hunger is a physical feeling that comes on gradually, not a thought that appears suddenly.

Heart: Focus on your feelings. What emotions are you experiencing at the moment? Let go of any negative thoughts or feelings you're having about eating; just stay curious and notice. (Note: You might be hungry *and* experiencing a particular emotion; awareness is helpful because your emotions may affect the rest of your eating decisions.)

How Hungry Am I?

As you become used to recognizing hunger, you'll see notice that there are different levels. They will help you decide when to start eating and when to stop. Use the Hunger and Fullness Scale to identify your hunger levels before, during, and after eating. The scale is not intended to set strict guidelines about when you should eat but rather, to help you develop awareness of your body's own signals and how different types and amount of food affect you.

The Hunger and Fullness Scale

Ravenous	Starving	Hungry	Pangs	Satisfied	Full	Very Full	Discomfort	Stuffed	Sick
1	2	3	4	5	6	7	8	9	10

Here are some descriptions to help you learn what the numbers mean:

Ravenous: Too hungry to care what you eat. This is a potentially high risk time for overeating.

Starving: You feel you must eat NOW!

Hungry: Eating would be pleasurable, but you could wait longer.

Hunger pangs: You're slightly hungry; you notice your first thoughts of food.

Satisfied: You're content and comfortable. You're not hungry or full—you can't feel your stomach at all.

Full: You can feel the food in your stomach.

Very full: Your stomach feels stretched and you feel sleepy and sluggish.

Uncomfortable: Your stomach is too full and you wish you hadn't eaten so much.

Stuffed: Your clothes feel very tight and you're very uncomfortable.

Sick: You feel sick and/or you're in pain.

? How do you feel physically and emotionally, *and* what happens when…

… you are at a 5 or above when you start to eat?

… you are at a 4 when you start to eat?

… you are at a 2 or 3 when you start to eat?

… you are at a 1 when you start to eat?

… you are at a 5 or 6 when you stop eating?

… you are at a 7 or higher when you stop eating?

Hunger Rhythms

Now that you know the basics of hunger, there are other factors that can help you understand and use your personal hunger rhythms.

- Hunger doesn't follow a clock, but you're in charge of adapting your meals to fit your hunger rhythms or adapting your hunger rhythms to fit your schedule.
- Hunger may seem erratic.
- Use hunger and fullness to establish a consistent meal pattern.
- Hunger is affected by what you eat and how much you eat.
- Hunger may be specific for a certain type of food.
- It may take 20 to 30 minutes after eating to tell you are full.
- Hunger cannot be satisfied before it occurs. That's called preventive eating.
- Hunger can be postponed until it is more convenient to eat.

? Think of specific personal examples of the hunger rhythms listed above. How does listening to your body help you eat in more satisfying ways?

 ## Nourish: Rediscover Food

Many people confuse restrictive eating with healthy eating. Labeling foods "good" or "bad" is one of the many habits we've picked up from dieting that often backfires.

? Make lists of foods that you think of as:

<u>Good</u>   <u>Bad</u>

? Look at the foods on your lists. Why did you label each food this way? Are you certain that these labels are completely accurate? Why or why not?

? When you eat a food from the "bad list," how do you feel? What happens?

All Foods Fit

Labeling particular foods as "bad" and attempting to avoid them can lead to feelings of deprivation, increased cravings, and ultimately, overeating. This usually increases guilt, frustration, and feelings of hopelessness. When you place food on a pedestal you give that food more power over you.

We've found it far more effective to use an "all foods fit" approach. In other words, instead of placing certain foods on a pedestal, you are free to choose from all foods based on your own experiences. You're less likely to crave or overeat certain foods simply because they're off limits. You're back in charge instead of trying to stay in control. With an all foods fit foundation, you can use the following three principles to answer just about any question you have about what to eat:

Balance: Be flexible with your food choices to balance your intake of food from all the food groups. It's also important to balance eating for nourishment with eating for enjoyment.

Variety: Focus on eating a variety of different foods to increase your nutrient intake, prevent monotony, and increase enjoyment.

Moderation: Moderation refers to how much and how often you eat certain foods. There's no need to weigh and measure food; the best way to determine if you've had enough is to listen to your cues of hunger and satiety.

? Are there any specific steps you want to experiment with to improve the balance, variety, and moderation in your eating this week?

 ## Live: Change Your Mind

? Think about exercise for a moment and write down everything that comes to mind.

Now take a look at what you wrote and answer these questions:

- Are your thoughts about exercise negative and limiting or positive and powerful?
- What feelings do those thoughts stir up?
- What do you do (or not do) as a result of those thoughts?
- What results do you get?
- How do you end up proving your thoughts right?

Are Your Thoughts on Your Side?

Your thoughts are so powerful that when you have negative thoughts about physical activity like "hate," "should," "lazy," your brain will seek evidence to prove that they are accurate. For example, when you say, "I'm lazy," you'll behave in a way that supports that definition of yourself, so you'll end up proving yourself right.

Beliefs
and
Thoughts

Results

Feelings

Actions

Whether we are talking about exercise, eating, or any other aspect of your life, remember that your beliefs and thoughts lead to your feelings, which lead to your actions, which lead to your results (TFAR). The intention then is to change your limiting thoughts to more powerful, effective thoughts that will lead to the results you want.

Choose More Powerful Thoughts

Compare common limiting thoughts with more powerful thoughts, then add your own:

Negative, limiting thoughts	Positive, powerful thoughts
I know I should exercise, but I hate it, so I just can't seem to make myself do it.	I enjoy becoming more physically active each day.
I don't know if exercise is really worth the effort.	I deserve all the amazing benefits I get from being physically active.
I don't have time.	I make time for my health and well-being.
I don't have the energy.	I feel myself becoming healthier and more energetic each day.
I'll start exercising when I've lost some of this weight.	Activity makes me healthier and more energetic no matter what I weigh.
Exercise is too hard for me.	I have more stamina, strength, and flexibility every day.
I'm too embarrassed to be seen exercising.	I exercise to take care of me.
I'm so out of shape, I don't even know where to start!	I have to start somewhere!
I can't do what they recommend so why bother?	I do what I can to become more fit and healthy.
I have a strenuous job, so I don't need to exercise when I get home.	I am building a great overall fitness plan for myself.

I was doing pretty well until I got sick (or busy, or company came, or I went on vacation…)	I have a flexible, consistent exercise plan.
I started exercising but I quit because I wasn't seeing the weight loss I expected.	I feel so good when I move my body.
I already exercise but I am still overweight.	I challenge my body to become healthier and more energetic to feel my best.
I used to be so athletic in high school; now I'm just a fat, lazy bum!	I'm not trying to compete in sports; I just want to be more active.
I can't exercise because it's too cold (or hot) outside.	I have a lot of options for staying active even when circumstances aren't ideal.

? What other negative thoughts or self-talk do you have about exercise, eating, or other areas of your life? What are more positive, effective thoughts?

? Picture yourself as a fit and active person. In colorful detail, describe what your life looks like:

Fitness Rx: Write an Exercise Prescription

Write your own exercise prescription. Include types you might enjoy, the desired benefits, and the dosage.

Refill: _Frequently_ Signed_____ Date _____

 Action Plan

- Set aside 15-30 minutes each day for reading, journaling, and reflecting on this process.
- Use Chapter 2 of your *Awareness Journal* to write down your observations and insights.
- Before you eat, ask yourself, *Am I hungry?* and practice identifying the physical signs of hunger.
- Give yourself a "Hunger and Fullness" number before, during and after eating.
- Begin to identify where those other urges to eat are coming from.
- Use the principles of balance, variety, and moderation to guide eating.
- Become more aware of your thoughts about physical activity.
- Think, *I am a fit and active person* and see what happens!

 My Intention for the Week

Awareness Journal

Date_____

Time	Why?	When?	What?	How?	How much?	Where?	Notes

Mindful Moment

When you wait until you're hungry, eating is more pleasurable and satisfying. Hunger is truly the best seasoning.

Awareness Journal   Date _____

Time	Why?	When?	What?	How?	How much?	Where?	Notes

Mindful Moment
When you don't overfill your stomach, you'll feel energetic and comfortable after eating.

Awareness Journal

Date _____

Time	Why?	When?	What?	How?	How much?	Where?	Notes

Mindful Moment
If you aren't hungry when you start eating, how will you know when to stop?

Workshop 2
Trust Your Body Wisdom

Awareness Journal

Date _____

Time	Why?	When?	What?	How?	How much?	Where?	Notes

Mindful Moment

Your thoughts lead to your feelings, which lead to your actions, which lead to your results. If you don't like your results, ask yourself what you were thinking first.

Awareness Journal　　Date _____

Time	Why?	When?	What?	How?	How much?	Where?	Notes

Mindful Moment
Start thinking of yourself as a fit and active person— and you will become one!

Awareness Journal

Date _____

Time	Why?	When?	What?	How?	How much?	Where?	Notes

Mindful Moment

When you're hungry, instead of using a long list of restricted and allowed foods, keep in mind the principles of Balance, Variety, and Moderation to guide your choices.

Awareness Journal   Date_____

Time	Why?	When?	What?	How?	How much?	Where?	Notes

Mindful Moment

Repeat encouraging thoughts frequently and you'll begin to notice more positive feelings, More effective behaviors, and more powerful results.

 Reading: Eat What You Love, Love What You Eat

 My Workshop Notes:

Think: When Do I Want to Eat? Part II

I'm Not Hungry. What Now?

? Whenever you want to eat, ask yourself, "Am I hungry?" Why didn't we say, "If you aren't hungry, don't eat"?

? When you recognize that a desire to eat isn't due to physical hunger, what are your options?

Weigh Your Options

Eat Anyway – Yes, this *is* an option! Even people who eat instinctively sometimes eat when they aren't hungry. Remember you're in charge. If eating isn't an option, then you're in a Restrictive Eating Cycle, usually leading to more eating.

Redirect Your Attention – Find something to do until the urge passes or you get hungry.

Meet Your True Needs – Figure out why you want to eat and do something to meet that need instead. We'll use a strategy called FEAST which is an acronym for Focus, Explore, Accept, Strategize, and Take Action; more on that later.

Option 1: Eat Anyway

? When you're in charge, you make decisions with full awareness. What are the advantages and disadvantages of eating anyway when you *aren't* hungry?

Advantages

- It's easy - no effort, thought, or energy required because you've done it many times.
- Gives temporary pleasure – for example, reward or celebration.
- Gives temporary distraction – for example, postpones doing something; avoid or distract yourself from a feeling.

Disadvantages

- Discomfort – both physical (stuffed) and emotional (regret). Note: Regret is different from guilt; no need to feel guilty if you made a conscious choice to "eat anyway." Guilt often just leads to more overeating.
- Your body stores it. When you eat food your body didn't tell you to, it will save it for later which may cause decreased energy.
- Unmet Needs – When you attempt to meet your needs with food, you're not truly meeting your needs. When your true needs are unmet, your triggers will return again and again.

Option 2: Redirect Your Attention

? What are the advantages and disadvantages of redirecting your attention when you aren't hungry?

Advantages

- Urge to eat will likely pass
- More productive use of time than eating.
- Disrupts your Overeating Cycle.
- Especially useful for environmental triggers.
- You'll eat when you're hungry—and then it will be more satisfying.

Disadvantages

- Requires some thought and effort.
- Requires some preparation.
- Temporary distraction – fine if there was an environmental trigger that will pass by.
- May not meet your true needs.

Strategies: Redirecting Your Attention

- Make a list of redirection activities (see 101 Things to Do Besides Eat).
- Choose activities that are enjoyable, like a new hobby.
- Strive to find activities that revitalize, relax, or nurture you.
- Choose activities that are "eating incompatible" – you can't eat while you do them.
- Have some activities that are simple and quick and some that are more time-consuming so you'll have activities for a variety of situations.
- Promise yourself that you'll try redirection for at least at little while.
- Be prepared with things to do and have the necessary supplies on hand.
- Create a Redirection Kit with the things you need to redirect your attention from food, like stationary, craft supplies, an inspirational book, your journal, cards, etc.
- Establish a food-free Self-Care Zone at home and at work.
- Create "rules" for yourself if they're helpful: "I'll redirect my attention for 10 minutes before I decide whether to eat."

In the following table, list a variety of redirection activities under each heading. When you're finished, go back through your lists and put a number by each activity indicating the following:

1 = Sounds great

2 = Sounds good

3 = Tolerable

Cross off any activities that aren't at least tolerable. (If your choice was between eating or doing something you dread, what would you be most likely to choose?) Strive to have plenty of "1"s and some "2"s, and fewer "3"s. Also, make a note by activities that are good for certain situations, i.e. while you're at work.

Simple/Quick	Complex/Time Consuming
1 Call a friend (home/work)	3 Organize a closet (home)

Redirecting your attention is not punishment; you're not distracting yourself to deprive yourself. The intention is to redirect your attention until you're actually hungry. Distraction is most effective when your trigger is boredom, an environmental trigger, or when you aren't able to sort through or meet your true needs right then. However, if you always choose to distract yourself and never address the underlying trigger, it will continue to cause an urge to eat... which brings us to your third option:

Option 3: Meet Your True Needs

? What are the advantages and disadvantages of meeting your true needs when you want to eat but you're not hungry?

Advantages
- Decreases triggers - Discovering what is triggering the urge to eat and addressing the underlying need will eventually cause that trigger to significantly decrease.

- When your true needs are recognized and met, you move toward optimal well-being.
- Leads to the best long-term results.
- The process will also help you learn how to deal with other issues in your life.

Disadvantages

- Most challenging (but also the most rewarding!)
- Requires time, effort, and energy.
- Requires openness and honesty with self, and often, with others.
- May require the assistance of others to work through issues and develop new skills.

When a craving doesn't come from hunger, eating will never satisfy it.

When you don't meet your true needs, those unmet needs can actually drive your Overeating Cycle. Clearly, this is the most effective option, though not always the easiest.

Struggling with overeating doesn't mean that you have a dark, deep psychological issue. It often means that you have learned to cope with certain situations or emotions in certain ways. But at least you've been coping—and now you can find new ways.

However, sometimes there is an underlying issue that needs to be dealt with. Examples include symptoms of depression, anxiety, an eating disorder, or other problems that indicate a need for additional help. Seek the advice of a health care professional if your symptoms persist. There *is* effective treatment available.

FEAST

Using the acronym FEAST, there are five steps you can take to help you become aware of *why* you want to eat even though you aren't hungry. It also helps you take small steps toward meeting that need. **FEAST** is Focus, Explore, Accept, Strategize, Take action.

F = Focus

The first step is to focus and tune into your body, your thoughts, and your feelings without judgment. Start with a Body-Mind-Heart Scan:

Pause. Move away from food, close your eyes, and take a few deep breaths.

Body: Focus on your physical state. Are you hungry or full? What is your hunger number? Do you notice any particular areas of your body? Are there any areas of discomfort? Does your body feel good?

Mind: Focus on your thoughts. What is going through your mind? Don't worry about what the thoughts are; just observe them floating by.

Heart: Focus on your feelings. What emotions are you aware of? For example, is there any sadness, anger, guilt, fear, or happiness? Complete the sentence: I feel _____ or I am _____. Feelings can usually be described in a word or two, whereas thoughts are sentences or phrases.

? What are some other ideas for ways you can get in touch with what you're thinking and feeling?

Here are a few other suggestions: Journal; talk it through with a friend or counselor; draw or scribble; notice if the cravings give you clues; imagine someone helping you, like a parent or a trusted friend. Perhaps you can tap into how you parent your children or manage your employees consciously and compassionately.

E = Explore

Once you are aware of your physical sensations, thoughts, and feelings, you can begin to explore them—*without* judgment. Your triggers can be physical, environmental, or emotional. Some are learned habits, like eating popcorn at the

movies. Other triggers are more significant, like an attempt to cope or meet important needs, and therefore require more exploration. We'll explore common triggers and strategies for dealing with them in the next workshop.

A = Accept

Accept things as they are right now. Resisting the situation or how you feel, doesn't make it go away—it just increases your struggle. Let go of thoughts of right or wrong, bad or good, should or shouldn't have. Be nurturing and supportive toward yourself. Do you feel more calm and able to cope?

S = Strategize

Be a problem solver; come up with as many creative solutions as you can to address the trigger. Examples: Just breathe; try a hobby; make a new friend; talk to a friend or co-worker; buy a book on the subject; discuss your concerns with the person directly; see a counselor. Don't worry about making the right choice; just make adjustments until you figure out what works for you.

T = Take Action

This is about being in charge. Take a step in the direction you wish to go—no matter how small the step seems.

? What did you learn by using FEAST when you felt like eating when you weren't hungry? Is there anything different you'll try next time?

Though it's more challenging to go through the steps outlined in FEAST, it will give you the best long-term results. You'll learn to recognize your true needs and meet them more effectively. You may be surprised at how quickly your urge to eat diminishes and how much better you feel overall.

101 Things to Do Besides Eat

When you recognize that you want to eat in response to a trigger rather than true hunger, you can choose to do another activity to redirect your attention until the urge passes. Highlight the ideas that appeal to you and add some of your own. Choose activities that are enjoyable, available, and preferably, eating incompatible. Create a "Redirection Kit" or drawer with everything you need to distract yourself. Establish a food free Self-Care Zone that's perfect for these moments.

Imagine a more energetic you • Walk around the block • Call a friend • Make a list of your Top Ten Reasons to get active • Read a child a book • Make a To Do list • Dance a little • Plan a vacation • Get a massage • Jot a thank you note to someone • Go to bed early • Read a great book • Write in your Awareness Journal • Give yourself a manicure or pedicure • Plan a balanced meal for your family • Surf the Internet • Finish an unfinished project • Walk your dog • Feel your feelings • Volunteer in your community • Start a hobby • Brush your teeth • Tape your favorite show to watch while exercising • Take 5 slow, deep cleansing breaths • Practice an instrument • Balance your checkbook • Plan a party • Say a prayer • Buy yourself some flowers • Do a few sit-ups • Make a phone call to someone you like • Chop veggies to add to your dinner • Set your priorities • Try a new hairstyle • Give a massage • Write down something you are proud of this week • Clean out a junk drawer • Play a game with your kids • Try a new route on your walk • Scream! • Plant fresh herbs to use in your cooking • Drink a glass of water • Kiss someone • Try on some clothes • Catch up on your reading for work • Look at old pictures • Rent a video • Smell the roses • Wash your car • Chew gum • Plan a date for someone special • Swim a few laps • Read Eat What You Love, Love What You Eat • Take a hot, soothing bath • Update your calendar • Get it off your chest • Build something • Check in on an elderly person • Work in your yard • Start your holiday shopping list • Count your blessings • Write a letter • Fold some laundry • Notice your inner conversations • Take a nap • Run an errand • Work on your budget • Take a bike ride • Check your e-mail • Give your dog a bath • Make a positive statement about yourself and repeat often • Start a project you've been wanting to get around to • Send a birthday card • Meditate • Try a new recipe • Play cards • Set your goals • Freshen your make-up • Hug someone • Rearrange some furniture • Go take a hike! • Help with homework • Light a fire or some candles • Say "STOP!" out loud • Organize your photos • Walk around your workplace • Try a new relaxation technique • Talk it over with someone • Get a head start on your taxes • Do a "Honey Do" • S-t-r-e-t-c-h • Say what's on your mind • Pick up your mail • Straighten a closet • Think • Do something nice for someone anonymously • Check the stock market • Plan a romantic encounter • Clean out a file • Tell someone how you really feel • When you become truly physically hungry, eat!

Nourish: Drink and Be Merry

You won't get a list of rules to follow about what to eat, so you'll get to make your own choices. That means you'll need to understand your options and how they affect your body.

There are six major classes of nutrients: water, carbohydrates, protein, fat, vitamins and minerals. They're all important for your health! We'll start with water.

Why Is Water Important?

About 60-70% of your body is water. Water helps with blood flow, digestion, transporting nutrients, and regulating body temperature.

How Much Do I Need?

Rule of thumb = Drink 8 to 12 8-ounce glasses per day.

Better indicator = The color of your urine. When you're well hydrated your urine will be dilute and appear pale colored. (Note: supplements and medications can darken urine).

How Do I Optimize My Intake of Fluids?

? How could you improve the quantity and quality of the fluids you consume?

Balance
- Keep water handy. You will not drink it if it's not easily accessible.
- Be aware of salt, caffeine, and alcohol which can affect your fluid balance.
- Drink more during exercise, warm weather, and illness.

Variety

- If plain water isn't appealing at first, most people develop a taste for it.
- Eventually you'll find that water really satisfies thirst best.
- Most people enjoy their water more when it's cold.
- Spice it up with a splash of lemon, lime, cranberry juice, cucumber, or mint.
- You can also get fluid from foods like soups, salads, fruits, and vegetables. A bowl of clear broth soup before a meal has been shown to decrease intake.

Moderation

- Moderation – What "foods" are you drinking? Many liquids like juice, smoothies, and coffee drinks have as many calories as a serving of food—or an entire meal!
- Determine if drinking satisfies hunger as well as eating actual food. For example, you might find that having a glass of water and an orange is more satisfying than a glass of orange juice.

The Bottom Line for Fluids
How will you use balance, variety, and moderation to optimize your intake of fluids?

Balance:

Variety:

Moderation:

Live: Lay Your Foundation

What Moves You?

If you are considering increasing your physical activity, or making another change, identify your own powerful motivators by answering these two questions:

? Why is it important to me to make a change?

? Why do I want to make this change now, at this point in my life?

Ask these questions a few times to get to your personal motivators and powerful fuel for change. You'll know you've got it when you feel a strong emotion.

Set Your Intention

Intention setting is the practice of living in alignment with your values *now*. Your focus is on *being* based on the internal state you wish to create.

? Describe your intention for becoming more active. Make it so clear that you can see it and feel it vividly

Now create a plan for living out your intention. Setting a clear goal will give your brain a detailed map for your brain to follow.

Set a goal. Write your goal in positive, present terms using details (or pictures).

Start small: Break your goal into small, specific steps that you feel confident you can achieve. (Hint: If you're having difficulty reaching a particular goal, break it into even smaller steps.)

Consistency and flexibility: When life gets in the way (and it will!), how will you adjust so you can still fit fitness in? Be flexible but watch for detours.

Reward yourself: Eventually, you'll look forward to being more acitve, but in the meantime, what small and large incentives would help keep you motivated? (Examples: money, time.)

Use reminders: How can you remind yourself about your intention? (Examples: Vision board, inspirational notes, text messages.)

Set yourself up for success: Identify potential obstacles and possible solutions. The difference between achieving your goals or not is how you recover from the inevitable challenges.

Team up: Consider whether an exercise buddy, an exercise class, online community, friendly competition, or a personal trainer could help you.

Have fun! How can you keep fitness enjoyable, interesting, challenging, and rewarding?

? Now, what *one* specific step will you take in the next 24 hours?

The FITT Formula

If you are ready to set your intention to increase your physical activity, the FITT Formula is a simple format for setting specific, measurable goals.

 **Fitness Rx: The FITT Formula**
Use the FITT Formula to tailor a fitness program to your personal health needs, preferences, lifestyle, and goals.

Frequency: How often will you be active?

Intensity: How much effort will you use during your activity?

Time: How much time will you invest in being active?

Type: What kinds of activities will you do?

Action Plan

- Set aside 15-30 minutes each day for reading, journaling, and reflecting on this process.
- Use your Awareness Journal to write down your observations and insights.
- Make your list of "Things to Do Besides Eat" and create a Redirection Kit to keep all your supplies handy.
- Establish a food free Self-Care Zone in your home and at work.
- Identify at least one need that has been triggering your overeating and take specifics steps for meeting that need more effectively using FEAST.
- Improve the quality and quantity of fluids you drink.
- Set your intention and work through the goal setting process.

My Intention for the Week

Awareness Journal

Date _____

Time	Why?	When?	What?	How?	How much?	Where?	Notes

Mindful Moment

It's not necessary to make a perfect choice every time in order to break the eat-repent-repeat cycle. It's a matter of becoming aware, recognizing that you have choices, and taking small steps toward meeting your true needs.

Awareness Journal

Date _____

Time	Why?	When?	What?	How?	How much?	Where?	Notes

Mindful Moment

Set your intention to live in alignment with your values based on the internal state you wish to create. Then write powerful goals to give your brain a clear map to follow.

Awareness Journal   Date_____

Time	Why?	When?	What?	How?	How much?	Where?	Notes

Mindful Moment

Eating to deal with certain emotions is simply a way of coping. Once you're aware of how you're using food, you have an opportunity to meet your needs in more effective ways.

Awareness Journal

Date _____

Time	Why?	When?	What?	How?	How much?	Where?	Notes

Mindful Moment

If you continually struggle with fatigue and lack of stamina, you may be living in a state of slight dehydration. Imagine being able to boost your energy level just by consuming enough fluid.

Awareness Journal   Date_____

Time	Why?	When?	What?	How?	How much?	Where?	Notes

Mindful Moment
Put a sign on your refrigerator that says,
"If I'm not hungry, what I need isn't in here."

Awareness Journal   Date _____

Time	Why?	When?	What?	How?	How much?	Where?	Notes

Mindful Moment
You can eat when you aren't hungry—just be aware that you're doing it and try to understand why.

Awareness Journal

Date _____

Time	Why?	When?	What?	How?	How much?	Where?	Notes

Mindful Moment

Don't wait for the perfect time to begin exercising. It's unlikely that the perfect time will ever come—and it won't last forever anyway. Find a way to make fitness fit in just the way your life is today.

 ## Reading: Eat What You Love, Love What You Eat

Chapter 4   Think: When Do I Want to Eat? Part III
Chapter 12   Nourish: Clearing Carb Confusion
Chapter 20   Live: Increase Your Stamina

 ## My Workshop Notes:

Think: When Do I Want to Eat? Part III

What Am I Really Hungry For?

Head hunger is when you have thoughts about eating even when your body doesn't need food—or thoughts about continuing to eat after you've had enough?

? Make a list of all the triggers for overeating that you can think of. Indicate whether they are physical, environmental, or emotional triggers (these often overlap).

Strategies: Strategize and Take Action

Don't be surprised if at first you want to eat anyway. Eating is familiar and comfortable; change is uncomfortable at first. These strategies help get you through the necessary discomfort of change until the positive effects take over.

- **Be a problem-solver.** Consider all your choices and look for creative solutions.
- **Direction, not perfection.** Don't get trapped into thinking you have to do it perfectly. Instead, make a step, any step, in the direction you want to move.
- **Baby steps.** Recognize that reasonably-sized changes—even baby steps or micromovements, that you're willing to practice consistently will help you gradually rewire what feels good to you.
- **Be realistic.** Ask yourself, "Where is the door most open for me at this moment?" In other words, what can you realistically see yourself doing?
- **Pros and cons.** Consider the rewards and consequences of your options and think about the likely outcome of your decision.
- **No right or wrong.** There are no good or bad choices—just what's most effective for you under the circumstances.
- **Learn from your mistakes.** Every mistake brings you one step closer to being an expert in what works and what doesn't.
- **Practice, practice, practice.** Consistency and repetition are the keys to reducing the necessary discomfort of change.

Rewiring Your Brain

Our brains have a natural tendency to focus on our mistakes. We can replace this "mistake focused wiring" with "new behavior wiring" by mindfully noticing every new behavior we use. Whenever you make even a baby step, pause to soak in the awareness for at least 30 seconds. Notice your physical sensations, thoughts, and feelings. Record each of your new behaviors in your Awareness Journal daily to increase the likelihood that you'll repeat them in the future.

Physical Triggers

How have these common physical triggers for overeating affected you? What strategies can you come up with to deal with each trigger more effectively?

Thirst

Strategies:

Fatigue

Strategies:

Salivation

Strategies:

Urge to chew, crunch, or suck

Strategies:

Pain

Strategies:

Hormonal cycles

Strategies:

Medical conditions or Medication side effects

Strategies:

Environmental Triggers

Common cues for overeating include people, places, activities, and events that you associate with eating. Be creative when coming up with strategies for dealing with these common triggers.

Mealtimes/eating on a schedule

Strategies:

High-risk times

Strategies:

Holidays and weather

Strategies:

Preventive eating

Strategies:

Sight of food/food displays

Strategies:

Trigger foods

Strategies:

Advertising

Strategies:

Social events

Strategies:

Grocery shopping

Strategies:

Preparing food

Strategies:

Food associations

Strategies:

Mindless eating (eating in the car, talking on the phone)

Strategies:

Obligatory eating

Strategies:

Serving sizes

Strategies:

Dining out

Strategies:

Food in the workplace

Strategies:

Other:

Emotional Triggers

Identify emotions that trigger a desire to eat (including specific examples). Brainstorm better ways to distract, calm, comfort, and nurture yourself without turning to food.

Stress or overwhelm

Strategies:

Boredom

Strategies:

Pleasure and reward

Strategies:

Loneliness

Strategies:

Worry and tension

Strategies:

Sadness

Strategies:

Guilt and shame

Strategies:

Anger

Strategies:

Avoidance

Strategies:

Negative self-talk

Strategies:

Perfectionistic thinking

Strategies:

Communicating with body size

Strategies:

Diet mentality/deprivation

Strategies:

Eating disorders

Strategies:

Body dissatisfaction

Strategies:

Spiritual needs

Strategies:

Other:

Am I Hungry?
Mindful Eating Program

? Time to practice! Think about situations that trigger an urge to eat, then use this "fill-in-the-blank" formula. First, identify the trigger or the situation (when…) and the feeling (I feel…). Next, identify the underlying need (I need…) then one or more action steps you can take to meet that need (I will…).

When _____,

I feel _____.

I need _____.

I will _____.

When _____,

I feel _____.

I need _____.

I will _____.

When _____,

I feel _____.

I need _____.

I will _____.

 ## Nourish: Clearing Carb Confusion

Why Are Carbs Important?

Carbohydrates come from plants (or indirectly from plants in the case of dairy) and provide energy for your body to function. Carbohydrates are broken down glucose molecules that float around in your blood stream (also known as blood sugar) and can be stored in the liver and muscles in glycogen packets that can be used for energy when your blood glucose level falls. Many carbohydrate-containing foods are also nutrient rich.

What Are Carbs Anyway?

Simple Carbs

Simple carbohydrates are small packets of energy that are broken down easily and rapidly by your body. Simple carbohydrates include fructose found in fruits and honey, lactose found in dairy products, and sucrose found in table sugar, corn syrup, and some vegetables. They may give you a quick, short burst of energy and a sharp rise in your blood sugar—which may be followed by a rapid fall in blood sugar and energy, affecting your mood and leaving you feeling hungrier.

? To increase your awareness about the type and amount of simple carbs you eat, and how they affect your hunger levels, energy, mood, digestion, etc., review several days of your Awareness Journal. Write the following letters next to the simple carbohydrates you ate:

F Fruit
D Dairy
S Sugar

Now refer to the Fiber Content table in Eat What You Love, Love What You Eat and circle the simple carbohydrates you ate that contain fiber and estimate the number of grams in the serving you ate.

Complex Carbs

Complex carbohydrates are long chains of glucose in the form of starch and fiber.

Starch – found in grain and grain products (bread, cereal, pasta, rice, tortillas), vegetables, legumes (beans). Some of the nutrients and fiber are removed from highly processed foods, so look for "whole-grain" products.

Fiber – found with starches like grains, beans, and vegetables, and with fruit.
- Fiber is undigestible, so it is not broken down for energy.
- Fiber makes you feel fuller
- Fiber-containing foods cause a slower rise in blood sugar.
- Helps with digestion; helps keep you "regular."
- Recommended intake is about 25-30 grams/day.

? Review several days in your Awareness Journal to increase your awareness about the type and amount of complex carbs you eat, and how they affect you. Write the following letters next to the complex carbohydrates you ate:

WG   Whole Grains
RG   Refined Grains
L   Legumes
V   Vegetables

? Refer to the Fiber Content table in chapter 12 of Eat What You Love, Love What You Eat and estimate the number of grams of fiber in the serving(s) you ate. If needed, what changes could you make to increase your fiber?

Balance: Balance the types of carbs you eat and balance your carbs with other foods; for example, eat carbs with protein-containing foods to keep you satisfied longer, so you eat less.

Variety: Eat a variety of carbs for more nutrients and more enjoyment.

- Fruit recommendations: 2-3 servings a day. My intention: _____
- Dairy recommendations: 3 servings a day. My intention: _____
- Grain recommendations: at least 6 servings of grain or grain-products; at least 3 of those whole grain. My intention for whole grains: _____
- Vegetable recommendations: 3-5 servings a day. My intention: _____
- Fiber recommendation: 25-30 grams per day. My intention: _____

Moderation: Eat sugar in moderation; it can lead rapid changes in your blood sugar level which can affect your mood and leave you feeling hungrier.

The Bottom Line for Carbohydrates
How will you use balance, variety, and moderation to optimize your intake of carbs?

Balance:

Variety:

Moderation:

.

Live: Increase Your Stamina

Cardiorespiratory exercise: cardio = heart, respiratory = lungs. Cardiorespiratory exercise strengthens your heart and increases oxygen in your tissues.

? What types of activities increase your heart rate and make you breathe harder?

Why Bother?

? Which of the benefits of cardiorespiratory activity are important to you and why?

- Condition your heart, lungs and vascular system and lower your risk of heart disease
- Lower your blood pressure and resting pulse
- Raise your HDL cholesterol (the good kind that protects your heart)
- Increase your stamina
- Preserve lean body mass and strengthen major muscles
- Improve your sense of well-being, sleep, and energy levels

How Do I Get Started?

Walking is a great cardiorespiratory activity for most people because it's convenient, requires minimal equipment, and can be easily adjusted for any fitness level. However, you can apply this information to any type of cardiorespiratory activity.

Get FITT

Frequency: Aim for most days of the week.

Intensity: Adjust to your fitness level. Increase your walking intensity by moving your arms, walking uphill, or pushing a stroller.

Time: 10-60 minutes depending on fitness level; increase as your stamina increases.

Warm-up (5 minutes)

Brisk walk (5-60 minute)

Cool-down (5 minutes)

This sample Walking Schedule will help you choose the best place to start depending on your current activity.

WEEK	WARM-UP	BRISK WALK	COOL DOWN	TOTAL TIME	STRETCHING
1	5 min	5 min	5 min	15 min	After walk
2	5 min	7 min	5 min	17 min	After walk
3	5 min	10 min	5 min	20 min	After walk
4	5 min	12 min	5 min	22 min	After walk
5	5 min	15 min	5 min	25 min	After walk
6	5 min	18 min	5 min	28 min	After walk
7	5 min	21 min	5 min	31 min	After walk
8	5 min	24 min	5 min	34 min	After walk
9	5 min	27 min	5 min	37 min	After walk
10	5 min	30 min	5 min	40 min	After walk
11	5 min	33 min	5 min	43 min	After walk
12	5 min	35 min	5 min	45 min	After walk

Type: Walking is just one example; there are numerous options!

? If you use a fitness tracker, read "Strategies: Is Your Fitness Tracker Making Your Life Bigger or Smaller?" in Eat What You Love, Love What You Eat. Based on your answers, do you think your device is making your life bigger or smaller? Why? Will you do anything different based on this awareness?

Fitness Rx: FITT Formula for More Stamina
Use the FITT Formula to set goals for increasing your stamina.

Frequency:

Intensity:

Time:

Type:

©MMXVIII, Am I Hungry?, P.L.L.C.
www.AmIHungry.com

 ## Action Plan

- Set aside 15-30 minutes each day for reading, journaling, and reflecting on this process.
- Use your Awareness Journal to write down your observations and insights.
- Begin to identify your physical, environmental, and emotional triggers and build strategies for dealing with them.
- Aim to eat 5 fruits and veggies, 3 low-fat dairy, and 6 grains (3 whole grains) each day. Eat whole grains in place of refined grains when possible. Eat sugary foods in moderation.
- Gradually increase your fiber intake to 25 grams daily for women and 38 grams daily for men.
- Start or increase your walking or other cardiorespiratory activity. Use the walking chart or a pedometer to help you.

 ## My Intention for the Week

Awareness Journal

Date _____

Time	Why?	When?	What?	How?	How much?	Where?	Notes

Mindful Moment

When a craving doesn't come from hunger, eating will never satisfy it.

Awareness Journal

Date _____

Time	Why?	When?	What?	How?	How much?	Where?	Notes

Mindful Moment

Don't get trapped into thinking you have to do something perfectly. Instead, make a step, any step, in the direction you want to move.

Awareness Journal

Date_____

Time	Why?	When?	What?	How?	How much?	Where?	Notes

Mindful Moment

Recognize that reasonably-sized changes—even baby steps or micromovements that you're willing to practice consistently—are better than one huge temporary overhaul.

Awareness Journal

Date_____

Time	Why?	When?	What?	How?	How much?	Where?	Notes

Mindful Moment

Forget all or nothing. Become more active by starting wherever you are and increase gradually, step by step.

Awareness Journal

Date_____

Time	Why?	When?	What?	How?	How much?	Where?	Notes

Mindful Moment
There are no good or bad choices—just what's most effective for you under the circumstances.

Awareness Journal

Date _____

Time	Why?	When?	What?	How?	How much?	Where?	Notes

Mindful Moment

Cardiorespiratory activity provides you with numerous health benefits. Live longer and feel great—the perfect prescription.

Awareness Journal

Date _____

Time	Why?	When?	What?	How?	How much?	Where?	Notes

Mindful Moment

Sometimes, "I want food" really means, "I want love," "I want attention," "I want comfort," "I want rest," or "I want someone to listen to me."

 Reading: Eat What You Love, Love What You Eat

- Chapter 5   Think: What Do I Eat?
- Chapter 13   Nourish: Fat Facts
- Chapter 21   Live: Increase Your Flexibility

 My Workshop Notes:

Think: What Do I Eat?

On diets, there's a lot of emphasis on *what* to eat. What you eat is important—once you know *why* you're eating in the first place.

? Think about someone you know who eats instinctively. How do you think they decide what to eat?

When you're hungry, you get to decide what to eat. The most effective way to make permanent dietary changes is to learn to eat according to your body's signals and to eat as healthfully as possible *without* feeling deprived.

There are three questions to ask yourself to help answer the question *What do I eat?*

- What do I want?
- What do I need?
- What do I have?

What Do I Want?

? Why is it important to ask yourself what you want first? Describe a situation when you didn't eat what you really wanted. What happened?

- If you really want something, you'll eventually get around to eating it anyway. By then, you may be too full or feel too guilty to really enjoy it.
- Denying what you truly want typically causes overeating in the long-run.
- Satisfaction is not just physical fullness; it's also determined by whether you're enjoying the food you're eating.
- Your body has "wisdom" about what it needs.
- When you let go of "good food, bad food" thinking, foods lose their power, so it becomes easier to tune into your body's wisdom about what it needs.

What Do I Need?

Food decisions are not "good" or "bad" but some foods offer more nutritional benefits than others. As you consider what food to choose, ask yourself, "What does my body need?"

? What factors do you consider when deciding what you need to eat?

Use the following guide to help you select your next meal.

Balance, Variety, and Moderation. What else have you eaten today? What are you likely to eat later? Review your Awareness Journal; has your diet reflected the principles of balance, variety and moderation over the last several days?

My personal health inventory. Take an inventory of health issues to consider:

My medical issues (such as diabetes, high blood pressure):

My family history (such as diabetes, high blood pressure):

My allergies or reactions to certain foods:

My health goals:

Nutrition information. What nutrition information do you need to make an informed decision? Do not use it to deprive yourself or make yourself feel guilty.

Healthful alternatives. Remember, small, gradual changes make a big difference. Try new foods, new recipes, and use fresh ingredients. Ask yourself, "What's the healthiest choice I could make that won't leave me feeling deprived?"

What Do I Have?

? What foods could you keep on hand to eat when you're hungry? Make a list of foods to keep in your pantry, refrigerator, car, and/or desk at work.

Balance Eating for Nourishment with Eating for Enjoyment

? Describe your best day on a diet. What did you eat? Make a list of your meals and snacks from breakfast on.

? Describe your worst day of overeating. What did you eat? Again, make a list of meals and snacks from breakfast on.

? If you were going to create a day somewhere between those two extremes, a day where you ate healthfully but also ate foods you enjoyed, what and how much would you eat?

Can you imagine eating like this every day for the rest of your life? That's balancing eating for nourishment with eating for enjoyment. Learning to balance what you need with what you want is one of the most important keys to this process. That's how you find the smaller arc of your pendulum.

Strategies: Fearless Eating

? What are your "scary" foods—foods you've typically overeaten in the past?

To learn to eat those foods without bingeing, try the following steps and describe what happens.

- Choose one of your scary foods and give yourself permission to eat it when you really, really, really, really want it (The Four Really Test). Buy or prepare a single serving or a reasonable portion, or go out to eat it. Your choice:

- When you really, really, really, really want that food, eat it mindfully without distractions. Describe:

- Does it taste as good as you imagined? (If so, promise yourself you can have it again when you want it.) Describe:

- Are you aware of any fear-based thoughts that might prevent you from eating the foods you love and love the foods you eat? (Examples: "I shouldn't be doing this" or "I always binge when I eat this.") These thoughts can drive overeating and become a self-fulfilling prophecy. Write new fearless, supportive thoughts:

 ## Nourish: Fat Facts

Why are Fats Important?

- Promotes normal growth and development (especially in children).
- Helps absorb and transport certain vitamins (A, D, E, K).
- Provides energy for the body (9 calories per gram).
- Maintains healthy hair and skin.
- Improves flavor and texture in food and increases satisfaction from eating.

What is Fat Anyway?

Similar to carbs, there are different types of fats with different effects on the body.

Saturated fats

- Less healthy fats.
- Generally solid at room temperature.
- Found in animal products: butter, lard, cheese, fat on meat and poultry; and in tropical oils: coconut, palm, palm kernel oils.
- Remember: Saturated fats are Solid at room temperature and Sit in your arteries.

Unsaturated fats

- Healthier fats. Liquid at room temperature.
- Oils such as canola, corn, flaxseed, olive, peanut, safflower, sesame seed, soybean, and sunflower.
- Fatty fish such as salmon, tuna, mackerel and trout.
- Plant foods such as avocados, olives, nuts, seeds (like sunflower, sesame, pinenuts, pumpkin), peanut butter, and other nut butters.

Omega 3 fatty acids

- Omega-3 fatty acid, a type of unsaturated fat, is an "essential" fatty acid because it is necessary for health but your body cannot make it, so it must be consumed in food.

- Health benefits of omega-3 fatty acids include reducing inflammation, lowering triglyceride levels, slowing the buildup of plaque in the arteries, slight lowering of blood pressure, and reduction in risk of death from heart disease.
- Good sources include cold-water fish (such as salmon, tuna, trout, flounder, and halibut), flaxseed and flaxseed oil, chia seeds, canola oil, walnuts and walnut oil, and soybeans and soybean oils.

Trans Fats

- Manmade trans fats, formed from the partial hydrogenation of unsaturated fats, may increase inflammation and raise the risk of heart disease by lowering HDL (beneficial cholesterol), raising LDL (heart unhealthy cholesterol), and increasing triglycerides.
- They might be found in margarine, shortening, chips, snack foods, crackers, baked goods, and fried foods.
- Look for trans fat on the nutrition labels and look for "partially hydrogenated" oils in the ingredient list.

? To increase your awareness about the type and amount of fats you eat, review several days in your Journal. Write the following letters next to the different types of fat you ate:

SF	Saturated Fat
UF	Unsaturated Fat
O3	Omega 3s
TF	Trans Fat

? Review your intake. Are the principles of balance, variety, and moderation reflected in your choices?

? Do you plan to make any changes based on what you learned? If so, what are your specific goals?

The Bottom Line for Fats

How will you use balance, variety, and moderation to optimize your intake of fats?

Balance:

Variety:

Moderation:

 ## Live: Increase Your Flexibility

Stretching is a key part of a complete and balanced fitness program. Try this simple stretch break right now. Be gentle and listen to your body. Don't forget to breathe!

- Reach straight up over your head with both arms and really stretch. Hold. Can you feel tightness in your back? Now relax. Does it feel better?
- Push shoulder blades together. Hold. Relax.
- Drop your head forward toward your chest and hold. Next, drop your head back carefully and only as far as comfortable.

How do you feel? Isn't it amazing how a little stretching can make you feel good?

Why Bother?

- Decreases stiffness and tension.
- Increases range of motion.
- Promotes blood flow and nutrient supply to tissues.
- Prepares your body for exercise and reduces muscle soreness after exercise.
- Improves posture and balance and prevents injury.
- Decreases risk of lower back pain.
- Makes you feel good!

? What specific benefits might you gain from increasing your flexibility?

How Do I Get Started?

- Warm-up before stretching, such as a 3- to 5-minute walk; don't stretch cold muscles unless you are doing minor wake-up type stretches.
- Hold the stretch; don't bounce. Bouncing has a tighten-release effect that does not help lengthen the muscles. Try to hold each stretch for 20 seconds to relax the muscle completely.

- Listen to your body. If something is tight, pulling, or hurting, back off slightly until you're comfortable, then hold that position.
- Take deep breaths during stretching. Breathe in, then exhale slowly during the stretch. During the exhale, allow yourself to relax a little further into the stretch.

Get FITT

Frequency: 2-3 times per week.

Intensity: Stretching should be gentle and comfortable.

Time: A stretch session can take as little as 10 seconds to 20 minutes or more. Hold each stretch for 10 to 30 seconds.

Type: Stretch after exercise or stretch head to toe using the simple stretches on the following page. Try yoga, Pilates, a stretch class, or a video.

Fitness Rx: FITT Formula for More Flexibility
Use the FITT Formula to set goals for increasing your flexibility.

Frequency:

Intensity:

Time:

Type:

Flexibility from Head to Toe

Neck Stretch

Shoulder Stretch

Triceps Stretch

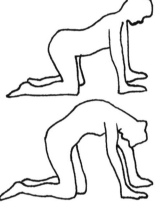

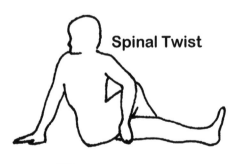

Cat Stretch

Lower Back Extension Stretch

Lower Back Flexion Stretch

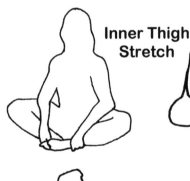

Inner Thigh Stretch

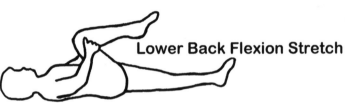

Spinal Twist

Shoulder Stretch

Calf Stretch

Thigh Stretch

©MMXVIII, Am I Hungry?, P.L.L.C.

www.AmIHungry.com

 ## Action Plan

- Set aside 15-30 minutes each day for reading, journaling, and reflecting on this process.
- Use Chapter 5 of your Awareness Journal to write down your observations and insights.
- Ask the three "Whats?" to help you decide what you'll choose to eat.
- Experiment with unsaturated fats, like balsamic vinaigrette made with canola oil, olive oil on bread, grilled fish, etc.
- Try stretching exercises twice this week and notice how you feel.

 ## My Intention for the Week

Awareness Journal

Date _____

Time	Why?	When?	What?	How?	How much?	Where?	Notes

Mindful Moment

Asking yourself "What do I want?" usually leads to more enjoyment and greater satisfaction. Remember the Four Really Test: "Do I really, really, really, really want _____?"

Mindful Eating Program

Awareness Journal

Date_____

Time	Why?	When?	What?	How?	How much?	Where?	Notes

Mindful Moment
Food decisions are not "good" or "bad." It all comes back to balance, variety, and moderation.

Awareness Journal

Date _____

Time	Why?	When?	What?	How?	How much?	Where?	Notes

Mindful Moment

Small sustainable changes are more effective than a large temporary overhaul. What is one small change you are willing to experiment with?

Awareness Journal

Date _____

Time	Why?	When?	What?	How?	How much?	Where?	Notes

Mindful Moment

A few moments of gentle stretching will relax your body *and* your mind.

Awareness Journal

Date _____

Time	Why?	When?	What?	How?	How much?	Where?	Notes

Mindful Moment

Do you keep a variety of satisfying foods on hand to eat when you're hungry?

Awareness Journal

Date _____

Time	Why?	When?	What?	How?	How much?	Where?	Notes

Mindful Moment

Nutrition information is a tool, not a weapon. Use it to make an informed decision— not to punish and deprive yourself or make yourself feel guilty.

Awareness Journal

Date _____

Time	Why?	When?	What?	How?	How much?	Where?	Notes

Mindful Moment

Shifting to liquid fats in place of solid fats may improve overall health while providing satisfying, flavorful foods.

 ## Reading: Eat What You Love, Love What You Eat

- Chapter 6   Think: How Do I Eat?
- Chapter 14   Nourish: Protein Power
- Chapter 22   Live: Increase Your Strength

 ## My Workshop Notes:

 ## Think: How Do I Eat?

Close your eyes and think about one of your most memorable eating experiences. Think about where you were, who was there, what you talked about, what the ambiance was like, what the food looked and smelled like, how it tasted, and how you felt.

? Now, pretend you're writing an article for a magazine. Write down as much detail about your dining experience as you can.

? How often do you have eating experiences like you described above? How often would you like to have experiences like that?

? Do you say you love food—but eat in a way that doesn't show it? What distracts you while you eat? Do you eat fast? Why?

? What happens when you eat "mindlessly"?

? Are you "mindless" in other areas of your life? What happens as a result?

Mindful Eating

Intention: Mindful eating is eating with *intention*—you're purposeful when eating:
- Eat when you're physically hungry.
- Eat to meet your body's needs for fuel, nourishment, and enjoyment.
- Eat with the intention of feeling *better* when you're finished.

Attention: Mindful eating is eating with *attention*—you focus fully on eating:
- Minimize or eliminate distractions.
- Tune into ambiance, aromas, flavors, temperature, and texture of the food.
- Listen to your body's cues of hunger and fullness.

Benefits of Mindful Eating

? What are some of the benefits you might experience from mindful eating?

- Increased enjoyment of food and pleasure and satisfaction from eating.
- Tune into hunger and fullness cues to stop at a comfortable level.
- Helps you notice how certain foods and situations affect you.

Strategies: Mindful Eating

With practice, mindful eating becomes natural. Set aside time to walk through the strategies for Mindful Eating by yourself or with a friend.

Why?

Why you are eating will affect every decision that follows. Are you eating for fuel, nutrition, pleasure, convenience, a trigger—or some combination?

When?

- When you have an urge to eat, pause and ask yourself, "Am I hungry?"
- Set your intention for how full you want to be when you're finished eating.

What?

Choose food that will satisfy your body and mind. Ask yourself:

- What do I want?

- What do I need?

- What do I have?

How?

- Create a pleasant environment. Set the table, put music on, maybe light candles.
- Minimize distractions such as television, driving, working, or reading.
- Sit down. Have only one or two places at home and work that you eat.
- Estimate how much food you'll need to eat for the level of fullness you're aiming for, then prepare, order, or serve yourself the amount of food you predict you'll need. Move or remove any excess.
- Create a real or imaginary "speed bump" by dividing your food in half on your plate.
- Center yourself by taking a few deep breaths. Try to stay calm throughout your meal.

- Take a moment to express gratitude.

? What are you thankful for?

? Closely look at your food. Which food do you eat first and why?

- Decide which food looks the most appetizing and take a few bites of that food first. If you save the best for last, you might eat it even if you're already full.
- Appreciate the appearance, aroma, colors, and textures of your food.
- Take small bites so you can fully taste and smell your food as you eat.
- Set down your fork down between bites.
- Stay connected and continue to enjoy the flavors, aromas, and textures.
- If the food doesn't taste as good as you thought it would, stop and choose something else if possible.

? Describe the appearance, aromas, textures, and flavors of your food.

How much?

- When you reach your speed bump, pause for a couple of minutes; recheck your Hunger and Fullness level. Don't be surprised if you're already full.
- Notice when your taste buds become less sensitive, signaling that you've had enough. (Be careful you're not "eating a memory" of what it tasted like.)
- When you feel satisfied, push your plate away, cover it with a napkin, or leave the table to indicate to yourself and others that you're done.
- Remind yourself that you'll eat again when you're hungry.
- Check your Hunger and Fullness level after eating and 20 minutes later.

- If you met your intention for how you wanted to feel, enjoy the feeling and acknowledge what you did to achieve this.

- If you overate, analyze what happened without judgment. Think about why you overate and what you'll do differently next time. Most importantly, don't give into paralyzing feelings of guilt. (We'll go into much more detail about this in the next workshop.)

? How did you feel when you reached your speed bump? How about when you were finished eating?

? What did you notice while eating mindfully?

? What other areas of your life would benefit from mindfulness? How could you use *intention* and *attention* in your relationships, work, leisure time, exercise, etc. to become fully present during those experiences?

Nourish: Protein Power

Why Is Protein Important?

- Protein helps build, repair, and maintain organ and muscle tissue.
- It's important for production of enzymes and hormones, immune system function, and fluid balance. It even helps maintain healthy skin and hair.
- Eating protein increases satiety—helps you feel fuller longer.
- Protein can also be used for energy. One gram of protein is broken down to provide 4 calories of energy.

What Is Protein Anyway?

Amino acids are the "building blocks" of protein. There are 20 amino acids: 9 essential (must be eaten) and 11 nonessential (can be made by your body).

Like the letters of the alphabet, they can be arranged to make (or "spell out") the proteins needed by your body.

- Animal (meat, poultry, seafood, fish, eggs, and dairy) and plant sources (soybeans, quinoa) are complete proteins that provide all 20 amino acids.
- Grains, beans, lentils, nuts, and seeds contain various essential amino acids so by eating a variety, you can consume all the amino acids your body needs.

How Do I Optimize My Protein Intake?

Balance

- An unbalanced diet can lead to boredom and nutrient deficiency.
- Eating protein throughout the day at meals and snacks increases satiety.

Variety

- Eating a variety of protein sources improves your intake of the amino acids and a variety of other nutrients. Red meat is high in iron, fish is high in omega-3 fatty acids, dairy is high in calcium, legumes are high in fiber, and nuts are high in beneficial unsaturated fats.

Moderation

Most people can meet their protein needs without protein supplements.

Examples of Protein Content

Source	Type	Amount of Protein per Serving	Serving Size
Dairy	Milk	8 grams	1 cup (8 oz.)
	Soft cheese (cottage or ricotta)	14 grams	1/2 cup (4 oz.)
	Hard cheese	5-7 grams	1 1/2 -2 oz.
	Yogurt	6-8 grams	8 oz.
	Ice cream	3-5 grams	1/2 cup
Eggs	Egg	6 grams	1
	Egg white	3.5 grams	1
	Egg substitute	5-6 grams	1/4 cup
Legumes	Beans or lentils	6-8 grams	1/2 cup
Meat, Poultry, or Seafood	Cooked lean meat, poultry or fish	6-9 grams per ounce	2-3 oz.
Nuts	Assorted nuts	6 grams	1 oz., 1/3 cup
	Peanut butter	8 grams	2 tablespoons
Soy	Soy, cooked	14 grams	1/2 cup
	Tofu	10 grams	1/2 cup

? Review several days in your Awareness Journal. Using the chart "Examples of Protein Content," write the following letters next to the different sources of protein and estimate the number of grams of protein you ate:

C (Complete Proteins): Dairy, Eggs, Meat, Poultry, Seafood, Soy, Quinoa
I (Incomplete Proteins): Legumes, Lentils, Nuts, Seeds, Grains

? Based on your Journal, what are your primary sources of protein? What is your average daily protein intake?

? Based on what you learned from reviewing your Awareness Journal, are there any changes you're going to make in your food selections?

? Are there any protein-containing foods you plan to experiment with during your snacks and meals to see if they increase satiety? Is so, record your results in your Awareness Journal.

The Bottom Line for Protein
How will you use balance, variety, and moderation to optimize your protein intake?

Balance:

Variety:

Moderation:

 ## Live: Increase Your Strength

Strength training or resistance training is any activity that requires a specific muscle group to work harder than it's used to. When repeated over time, those muscles will become stronger to handle the additional challenge.

? What are some examples of strength training activities?

- Lifting your own body weight (sit-ups or push-ups).
- Moving against the resistance of rubber tubing or a band.
- Lifting weights (including cans and jugs) or using exercise machines.
- Doing strength exercises using a stability ball which provides support and builds core strength.

Why Bother?

- Improves your function in your daily life and decreases your risk of injury.
- Maintains or boosts your metabolism by increasing your muscle mass.
- Improves your body composition by increasing your muscle mass and decreasing your body fat.
- Helps minimize loss of muscle tissue that can occur with weight loss.
- Helps prevent age-related loss of muscle mass and strength.
- Improves glucose metabolism, blood pressure, and cholesterol levels.
- Prevents or treats osteoporosis by increasing bone mineral density.
- Decreases lower back pain by increasing core abdominal strength.

? What specific benefits would you gain from increasing your strength?

Get FITT

Frequency—benefit occurs with strength training twice a week. Allow at least 48 hours before working a specific muscle group again.

Intensity—two to three sets of 8-20 repetitions for each exercise. If you can't do 8, the weight is too heavy; if you can do more than 20, the weight is too light.

Time—20-30 minutes per session.

Type—See the illustrations on the next page and the examples listed above.

Strength training isn't just for body builders. In fact, most people don't have the time it would take to become highly muscled, and women don't have the hormones to become bulky from working out. Strength training is really about increasing your muscle mass to boost your metabolism and function more fully in your life.

Fitness Rx: FITT Formula for More Strength
Use the FITT Formula to set goals for increasing your strength.

Frequency:

Intensity:

Time:

Type:

Am I
Hungry?
Mindful Eating Program

Simple Strength from Head to Toe

Squats

Push-ups

Superman

Leg Lifts

Bridge

Sit-ups

 ## Action Plan

- Use Chapter 6 of your Awareness Journal to write down your observations and insights.
- Identify your eating habits that might interfere with your ability to be mindful and experiment with possible solutions.
- Practice mindful eating several times this week by walking through the strategy step by step.
- Notice how protein affects your hunger and fullness levels.
- Consider adding a plant-based meal several times a week.
- Experiment with strength training exercises a couple of times this week.

 ## My Intention for the Week

Awareness Journal

Date _____

Time	Why?	When?	What?	How?	How much?	Where?	Notes

Mindful Moment

Choosing to eat mindfully—with intention and attention—will give you optimal enjoyment and satisfaction from eating.

Awareness Journal

Date_____

Time	Why?	When?	What?	How?	How much?	Where?	Notes

Mindful Moment

Eat without distractions so you can give food and your body's signals your full attention. If you love to eat, act like it!

Awareness Journal

Date _____

Time	Why?	When?	What?	How?	How much?	Where?	Notes

Mindful Moment

Decide how full you want to be when you're finished eating. If you don't have a plan, you're more likely to eat more than you wanted or needed to.

Awareness Journal

Date _____

Time	Why?	When?	What?	How?	How much?	Where?	Notes

Mindful Moment
Even when you're preparing food for yourself, make it attractive, as if you were serving it to someone special—because you are!

Awareness Journal

Date _____

Time	Why?	When?	What?	How?	How much?	Where?	Notes

Mindful Moment

If you eat while you're distracted by watching television, reading, driving, working, or talking on the telephone, you won't be able to give your food or your body's signals your full attention.

Mindful Eating Program

Awareness Journal

Date_____

Time	Why?	When?	What?	How?	How much?	Where?	Notes

Mindful Moment

Becoming mindful will bring greater satisfaction and more pleasure to eating *and* all other aspects of your life—your relationships, your work, your leisure activities and exercise.

Mindful Eating Program

Awareness Journal

Date_____

Time	Why?	When?	What?	How?	How much?	Where?	Notes

Mindful Moment

For a limited investment in time, strength training pays big rewards by improving your muscular strength and endurance so you can function more fully in your life!

 ## Reading: Eat What You Love, Love What You Eat

- Chapter 7   Think: How Much Do I Eat?
- Chapter 15   Nourish: It's the Little Things
- Chapter 23   Live: Challenge Your Body

 ## My Workshop Notes:

 Think: How Much Do I Need?

Think about what it means to be satisfied. *Satisfied* means that you simply don't need anything else—so you're left feeling content, fulfilled, pleased, or even happy—*just right*. How wonderful to feel satisfied when you're done eating!

Enough is Enough

Just as you use your Hunger and Fullness scale to let you know when to eat, you'll use it to let you know when you've had enough. To increase your awareness, develop the habit of giving yourself a Hunger and Fullness number in the middle of eating, at the end of your meal, and 20-30 minutes later.

? How does it feel when you are "just right"?

Remember, the purpose is to eat with intention—so before you start eating, decide how full you want to be when you're done. Estimate how much food you'll need to reach that level of fullness and serve or order the appropriate amount of food. If you were served, move any excess so you will consciously decide. Create a speed bump by physically or visually dividing the food in half. Check in when you reach the speed bump, then again when you're done eating.

How Full Am I?

4 or less = Still a little bit hungry. Your options:

- Wait awhile to see if your Hunger and Fullness number increases.
- Eat more now.
- Eat again in a while.
- Stop at a 4; this is a good idea if you plan to have dessert, if you'll be eating again soon, or when don't want to feel food in your stomach, like before exercise.

5 = Satisfied - Feels great! Remember this feeling:

- I'm not hungry and I feel comfortable.
- I don't feel the food in my body.
- I could eat more but I don't need to.
- The flavor of the food begins to fade.
- Harder to give every bite my full attention.
- I feel light and energetic and ready for my next activity.

6 = Full

- I can feel the food, but it is not unpleasant.

5 or 6 = I've had enough. Move away from the table, clear the food, clean the kitchen, cover your plate, package up leftovers for another meal.

7 to 10 = Very full to sick; "I ate too much."

? How do you feel physically and emotionally when you've eaten too much?

Don't Miss the Lesson

If you've eaten too much, turn the situation into a learning experience. Notice how you feel both physically and emotionally. Remember all the details so you can recall them the next time you're tempted to keep eating. Notice how you feel:

- Stuffed, bloated
- Nauseated or queasy
- Short of breath
- Sleepy, sluggish
- In the past, guilty

? In an Overeating Cycle, what typically happens when you overeat?

In an Overeating Cycle, guilt often leads to thoughts of "I already blew it—I might as well keep eating." Ironically, guilt fuels the Overeating Cycle.

? What is the difference between guilt and regret?

You are *in charge* so you can choose whether to overeat. You're not bad based on how much you eat—but you might *feel* physically bad—and therefore regretful. Regret leaves the door open for learning. When you overeat, don't beat yourself up. Instead, explore why it happened so you can learn from mistakes.

Why did it happen?

Review your last eating cycle and ask questions to help you determine why you overate:

Why? Why was I eating in the first place? Was I in an Instinctive, a Restrictive, or an Overeating Cycle?

When? When did I get the urge to eat? What was I thinking? What was I feeling? What else was going on? Am I able to identify hunger? Was I hungry? How hungry was I? Was I too hungry? If I wasn't hungry, what was the physical, environmental, or emotional trigger to eat?

What? What did I choose to eat and why? Did that affect how much I ate? Did I choose food that is satisfying? Did I like it? Did I feel guilty about my choice? Was I afraid I wouldn't get to eat it again? **How?** How did I eat? Was I mindful or was I distracted? Did I eat fast?

How Much? Did I set an intention for how full I wanted be when I was done eating? How much food did I have in front of me? Where there any physical, environmental, or emotional triggers for overeating?

Where? Where have I been investing my energy lately? Could that be why I overate?

? The next time you feel too full after eating, review your last eating cycle to uncover possible reasons.

Why?

When?

What?

How?

How Much?

Where?

What will I do differently next time?

Once you've recognized possible reasons for overeating, make a plan for what you will do differently next time.

? What could you do differently next time?

After you've gathered your lessons from the experience, let the overeating episode go and move on to your next eating cycle.

Strategies: I Ate Too Much! Now What?

? Do people who eat instinctively ever overeat? What do they do afterward?

Re-enter the Mindful Eating Cycle

Even people who eat instinctively sometimes overeat, but they don't feel guilty—just uncomfortable. They may naturally make up for occasional overeating by paying attention to their body wisdom.

Why? Eat to fuel and nourish your body.

When? Wait to see *when* you want to eat again. When you wait until you're hungry, you may find you don't want your next snack or meal as soon as usual.

What? Wait to see *what* you're hungry for. Don't punish yourself or try to compensate for overeating by restricting yourself. Instead, ask yourself, "What do I want?" and "What do I need?" Trust your body wisdom; it typically seeks balance, variety, and moderation, so you may want something small or something light after eating a heavy meal.

How? Eat with intention and attention; you'll be less likely to repeat your recent mistake.

How much? You may not be as hungry so pay attention to how much you serve, order, prepare, and eat.

Where? Don't use exercise to punish yourself for eating; instead, be active and use your fuel to live an active, vibrant life.

? Where else in your life can you apply the concept "Don't miss the lesson!"?

Workshop 7
Just Right

 ## Nourish: It's the Little Things

Why Are Micronutrients Important?

Compared to the macronutrients (carbohydrates, fats, and protein), these nutrients are needed in small amounts by the body, but they perform hundreds of critical functions.

What Are Micronutrients Anyway?

Micronutrients include vitamins, minerals, phytochemicals, and other small but important compounds found in food.

How Do I Optimize My Micronutrient Intake?

You probably don't need to track your intake of specific vitamins and minerals when you follow the principles of balance, variety, and moderation. There may be specific reasons your health care professional recommends a supplement, such as calcium with vitamin D, or recommends that you limit sodium to less than 2400 mg (about a teaspoon a day).

Balance
- Eat a balance of nutrient-rich foods.

Variety
- Variety is the key to consuming micronutrients. No single food has them all.
- Take advantage of fresh fruits and vegetables in season. Eat the skins and peels when possible, after washing of course. Don't overcook. If fresh isn't available, frozen is second best, canned next (but watch the sodium in canned vegetables and sugar in canned fruit).
- Go for color. Vitamins and phytochemicals are found in greater concentrations in brightly colored fruits and vegetables.
- Go for nutrient-rich foods like blueberries, cantaloupe, mangoes, tomatoes, broccoli, whole grains, nuts, and seeds.
- Experiment with new recipes.

©MMXVIII, Am I Hungry?, P.L.L.C.   Page 145   www.AmIHungry.com

Moderation

Moderation is not a concern with most micronutrients unless you're taking supplements. In that case, don't exceed the daily recommendations.

? Review your Awareness Journal. Do your choices reflect a variety of nutrient-rich foods? What changes will you make to help you get the most from your diet?

The Bottom Line for Micronutrients

How will you use balance, variety, and moderation to optimize your micronutrient intake?

Balance:

Variety:

Moderation:

Am I Hungry?
Mindful Eating Program

Live: Challenge Your Body

Essentials of Optimizing Your Fitness

We have been using the FITT principle to get the most from your physical activity. We've talked a lot about Frequency, Time, and Type so now let's focus on Intensity.

Intensity: Perceived Exertion Scale

The perceived exertion scale is similar to the Hunger and Fullness Scale. It encourages you to listen to your body to assess the intensity of your exercise.

Perceived Exertion Scale				
Minimal	Light	Moderate	Vigorous	Maximal
1 2	3 4	5 6	7 8	9 10

Intensity: Target Heart Rate Zone

To get the most benefits from aerobic exercise, exercise within your Target Heart Rate Zone (THR). This "challenges" your heart and lungs to work harder so they become stronger and more efficient.

? Practice checking your pulse, both at rest and with exercise. If it would be helpful, calculate your Target Heart Rate Zone and write it on an index card:

Estimated Maximal Heart Rate (MHR) = 220 – Your Age _____ = _____

Low end of your THR zone = 60% of MHR = 0.65 X _____ (MHR) = _____

High end of your THR zone = 85% of MHR = 0.90 X _____ (MHR) = _____

? How can you increase the intensity of your cardio activities to optimize your fitness?

? How can you increase your flexibility activities to optimize your fitness?

? How can you increase the intensity of your strength training to optimize your fitness?

? Are you interested in trying intervals (taking your heart rate from the low to the high end of your target heart rate several times during exercise.)

Fitness Rx: FITT for More of a Challenge
Use the FITT Formula to set goals for increasing the intensity of your exercise.

Frequency:

Intensity:

Time:

Type:

 Action Plan

- Use Chapter 7 of your Awareness Journal to write down your observations and insights.
- Before eating, decide how full you want to be when you're done.
- If your level of fullness exceeds your goal, look back at your last eating cycle to learn from the experience. Ask yourself why it happened and what you'll do differently next time. Then, re-enter the Mindful Eating Cycle: wait to see how long it takes to get hungry, notice what and how much you're hungry for, and eat mindfully to decrease the likelihood of repeating the mistake.
- Increase your intake of nutrient-rich foods.
- Challenge your body by increasing the intensity of your workouts.

 My Intention for the Week

Awareness Journal

Date_____

Time	Why?	When?	What?	How?	How much?	Where?	Notes

Mindful Moment

Think for a moment about what it means to be "satisfied"—you simply don't need anything else so you are left feeling contented, fulfilled, pleased, and even happy—just right!

Awareness Journal

Date _____

Time	Why?	When?	What?	How?	How much?	Where?	Notes

Mindful Moment

If you eat more than you need, you'll feel unnecessarily uncomfortable. Eating the right amount of food isn't about being good; it's about feeling good.

Awareness Journal

Date_____

Time	Why?	When?	What?	How?	How much?	Where?	Notes

Mindful Moment

Before you overfill your stomach, pause and take a deep breath. Ask yourself, "Is it really worth feeling uncomfortable when I'm done eating? Or would I rather feel good?"

Workshop 7
Just Right

Awareness Journal
Date _____

Time	Why?	When?	What?	How?	How much?	Where?	Notes

Mindful Moment
For best results, keep your fitness plan interesting, challenging, and efficient.

Awareness Journal

Date _____

Time	Why?	When?	What?	How?	How much?	Where?	Notes

Mindful Moment

Satiety is your body's signal that it doesn't need food. Discomfort is your body's signal that you're not listening.

Awareness Journal

Date _____

Time	Why?	When?	What?	How?	How much?	Where?	Notes

Mindful Moment
When you make a mistake, don't miss the lesson.

Awareness Journal

Date _____

Time	Why?	When?	What?	How?	How much?	Where?	Notes

Mindful Moment

You don't need an excuse to have a wonderful meal—so why use a special occasion as an excuse to overeat? Besides, why would you want to feel uncomfortable if the occasion is so special?

 ## Reading: Eat What You Love, Love What You Eat

- Chapter 8   Think: Where Do I Invest My Energy?
- Chapter 16   Nourish: A Flexible Approach to Self-Care
- Chapter 24   Live: On Your Terms

 ## My Workshop Notes:

Think: Where Do I Invest My Energy?

Where you spend your energy is about much more than just exercise. It's about everything you chose to do.

? Retake the assessment "Recognizing Your Eating Patterns" in Workshop 1 (cover your original answers) or online. What changes do you notice?

? Where did you spend your time and energy in your Overeating Cycle?

? Where did you spend your time and energy in your Restrictive Eating Cycle?

What Is Optimal Well-Being?

Mindful eating frees you up to spend your energy on building optimal well-being. Optimal well-being is the best state of physical, emotional, intellectual, and spiritual wellness that you can have given your current opportunities and limitations. When you care for all aspects of your well-being, you create a "self-care buffer zone" that helps you cope with emotional and environmental eating triggers as they arise.

Body	Mind
Heart	Spirit

Invest Your Energy in Optimal Well-Being

As you free yourself from overeating and restrictive eating, you can redirect your time and energy toward other more productive and satisfying pursuits.

Physical Well-Being

When asked about health, most people think about physical health first.

Ideas for Physical Self-Care

- Establish a safe and secure physical space.
- Take care of your health needs; get a check-up.
- Eat fresh, healthful, and interesting foods.
- Engage in enjoyable physical activities and exercise.
- Get rest and adequate sleep.
- Give and receive physical affection.
- Take a hot bath or long shower.
- Get a massage, manicure, pedicure, or facial.
- Spend time in nature (walk, hike, camp, sit).

? What ideas do you have for investing in your physical well-being?

Emotional Well-Being

Emotional well-being doesn't mean always being happy. Emotional wellness is the result of learning to embrace the full spectrum of emotions, identify and cope with stress and feelings, seek balance, know your limits, nurture yourself, and cultivate healthy relationships.

Ideas for Emotional Self-Care

- Release emotional energy by journaling, drawing, crying, screaming into a pillow, or talking to a friend or advisor.
- Spend quality time with family and friends.
- Build intimacy with your significant other.
- Practice effective communication.
- Set appropriate boundaries assertively.
- Read or listen to self-help and self-improvement material; attend workshops like this.
- Do relaxation techniques and manage stress better.
- Practice forgiveness (with others and yourself).
- "Clean out the refrigerator" – deal with or let go of "old" stuff.
- Allow yourself to be vulnerable.
- Seek counseling or therapy if needed.
- Parent yourself more effectively. Others parented you when you were a child. Now you must parent yourself as an adult. Even if your own parents made mistakes, you can choose more effective ways of taking care of yourself.

? What are your ideas for investing your emotional well-being?

Intellectual Well-Being

Intellectual well-being is how you think and much more. It includes your thoughts, growth, stimulation, creativity, challenge, and more.

Ideas for Intellectual Well-Being

- Remember that: Thoughts > Feelings > Actions > Results. Are your thoughts:
  - Negative or Positive?
  - Powerless or Powerful?
  - Self-Defeating or Affirming?
  - Outdated or Forward Thinking?
  - Generalities or Specific?
  - Limiting or Growth Oriented?
  - Problem Focused or Solution Focused?
  - Scarcity or Abundance Thinking?
- Examine your priorities and set your goals.
- Read interesting, challenging, or classic works.
- Learn something new: a new skill or language.
- Do brain teasers and play challenging games.
- Be creative: art, music, crafts, and hobbies.
- Visit museums or other novel places.
- Take classes or study your areas of interest.
- Participate in stimulating discussion groups.
- Explore occupational opportunities.
- Travel or explore new areas.

? What ideas do you have for investing in your intellectual well-being?

Spiritual Well-Being

Spiritual well-being may include religion, but it's really much more. It encompasses your sense of purpose, knowing that there is something greater than yourself, your connection and relationship with a higher power, and others, unconditional love and acceptance, contribution, joy, and peace.

Ideas for Spiritual Self-Care

- Be fully present and mindful in all that you do.
- Pray, meditate, and/or practice yoga.
- Spend time alone and quiet; seek solitude, connect with nature.
- Define your guiding principles.
- Write in a personal journal.
- Visit your place of worship (or find one).
- Read meaningful, inspirational works.
- Have an attitude of gratitude.
- Serve and contribute to others.
- Receive with grace.
- Practice kindness.

? What idease do you have for investing in your spiritual well-being?

? What does it mean to have an abundance—food, money, time, energy, joy, and love?

In terms of food, abundance means that there's plenty, so you don't need to eat it all right now. When you use abundance thinking instead of scarcity thinking you're able to let go of fear and competition and see possibilities instead.

? Are any areas—body, mind, heart, or spirit—calling for some attention in your life? Did one idea or another "speak" to you?

Balance, Variety, and Moderation In All Things

If you made a long mental "to-do" list, let it go. Self-care is not about spending an equal amount of time or energy in each area. It's about making the commitment to care for yourself the best that you can and meet your true needs. Strive for balance, variety, and moderation, not just in the way you eat, but also in the way you live your life.

? Choose one or more ideas or strategies that inspired you. Create a short but specific action plan for putting that idea into motion. What one thing will you do today to put your action plan into motion and bring balance into your life?

 # Nourish: A Flexible Approach to Self-Care

As you finish this workshop, you may be asking yourself, "What now?" You may even be a little concerned that you'll go back to your previous habits since that has probably happened after you went off diets in the past. But keep in mind, this *isn't* a diet. It's a new way of thinking that changes the way you eat and live.

Measuring Change

Here's another way of looking at what you've learned. Using the instructions that follow, place yourself on the graph below.

Self-Care vs. Neglect

On the horizontal line, think about how the decisions you make affect your well-being. At one end of the spectrum is self-care. Decisions that promote self-care will have the most desirable effects on your health. Obvious examples include exercising regularly and eating a balanced diet.

On the other end of the spectrum is neglect. You're neglecting yourself when your decisions ignore or disregard your best interests. Examples of neglect include eating an excessive amount of salt when you have a history of high blood pressure or eating too much before bed even though it gives you heart burn. At the extreme, neglect can even be abusive toward yourself.

Flexible vs. Rigid

On the vertical line, think about how you make your day to day decisions. At one end of the spectrum is flexibility. Flexibility allows you to adapt to any situation. Another way of thinking about flexibility is freedom, meaning that you can make any decision you choose at any given time.

On the other end of the spectrum is rigidity. Rigid decision-making is strict with no room for error or unexpected detours. For example, when you try to follow a diet rigidly, you strive to be perfect without making any mistakes or going off the plan.

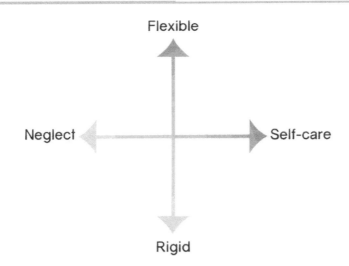

Where Are You Now?

The flexibility or freedom to do whatever you want without regard to your best interests can lead to overeating and inactivity. On the other extreme, rigid adherence to a food or exercise plan may improve your health but comes at a high price.

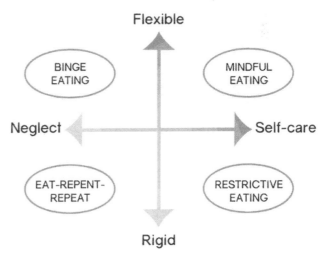

Since it is nearly impossible to rigidly adhere to any plan that feels harsh or restrictive, you may shift back and forth between an Overeating and a Restrictive Eating Cycle. Remember, we call that the eat-repent-repeat cycle. This pattern neglects your physical *and* your emotional well-being, and can lead to guilt, shame, and ultimately, failure.

On the other hand, when you're eating mindfully, you strive to take good care of yourself while giving yourself the flexibility to adapt your eating and activity to fit your personal preferences and changing circumstances.

What to Do When You Get Off Track (and you will!)

Unlike dieting, which often becomes more difficult over time, learning to eat mindfully becomes easier with practice. Choose to use every opportunity to learn more about yourself and why, when, what, how, and how much you eat—and where you invest your energy.

However, don't expect yourself to be perfect. It isn't possible—and it isn't necessary. You are in charge. Whenever you recognize that you are off track, notice which decision point you're at in your Mindful Eating Cycle and return to eating mindfully with the next decision you make.

? When you find yourself struggling with food or eating, use the Mindful Eating Cycle to notice where the problem is and help you get back on track:

Situation #1:

Why?

When?

What?

How?

How much?

Where?

Situation #2:

Why?

When?

What?

How?

How much?

Where?

A Lifelong Approach

You now have many new tools for your lifestyle management toolbox:

- You listen to your internal cues of hunger and satisfaction, instead of trying to follow strict or arbitrary rules about your eating.
- You build a strong foundation of nutrition information and choose from all foods freely to meet your needs instead of trying every fad diet that comes along.
- You're physically active because it gives you energy, stress relief, and an active metabolism instead of exercising to punish yourself or earn the right to eat.
- You eat foods you really enjoy *without* guilt, instead of depriving yourself or bingeing.
- You eat mindfully in a manner that nourishes your body, mind, and spirit instead of eating unconsciously or obsessing over every bite of food.
- You become aware of your thoughts, feelings, and actions and how they affect your results, instead of judging yourself because you didn't follow a program rigidly.
- You create a self-care buffer zone and meet your true needs instead of eating too much or neglecting yourself.

? Now you're in charge of using these tools to continue your journey toward a fulfilling vibrant life. What are you going to focus on next?

 ## Live: On Your Terms

Do What You Love, Love What You Do

Moving mindfully—in other words, choosing and doing physical activity with *intention* and *attention*—will help you discover physical activity that is both challenging and enjoyable, and help you appreciate your body's capacity to become stronger and healthier.

Move with intention. Be purposeful when you choose your activities.

- Choose activities that suit your personality and mood.
- Choose activities that meet your body's needs.
- Move with the intention of feeling *better* when you're finished.

Move with attention. Be attentive during your activities.

- Become aware of your surroundings, physical sensations, thoughts, and feelings.
- Listen to your body's cues of intensity, discomfort, and fatigue.
- Appreciate your body's stamina, flexibility, and strength.

Moving with Intention

? This week when you're thinking about exercising, choose the best activity for yourself by answering these questions:

What do I want to do?

What do I need to do?

What do I have to do?

? Take *Your Exercise Personality Quiz.* What did you learn about…

…why you exercise?

…how you prefer to exercise?

…when you like to exercise?

…where you prefer to exercise?

…who you like to exercise with (if anybody)?

…what you like to do for exercise?

? Based on what you learned about yourself, what will you do or do differently to create an enjoyable fitness program that fits your exercise personality?

Moving with Attention

Mindfulness during activity increases your awareness of your body, decreasing your risk of injury and boredom, increasing your enjoyment, and optimizing the time you invest. Most importantly, making a mind-body connection during exercise has a calming meditative effect that carries over into other aspects of your life.

? After exercising mindfully (including a Body-Mind-Heart scan), describe one session in detail.

Fitness Rx: On Your Terms
How will you increase your mindfulness during...

Lifestyle activity:

Cardio:

Flexibility:

Strength training:

 ## Action Plan

- Use Chapter 8 of your Awareness Journal to write down your observations and insights.
- Choose one or two specific ideas for improving your physical, emotional, intellectual, and/or spiritual well-being.
- Take the time to set your priorities and decide where you'll spend your energy this week.
- Don't expect yourself to be perfect. Stay aware and use your mistakes as learning opportunities by examining each decision point in your eating cycle.
- Become more mindful during exercise by using intention and attention.
- Continue to practice your new skills until they become second nature. Remember that this is a process, not a destination.

 ## My Intention for the Week

Awareness Journal

Date _____

Time	Why?	When?	What?	How?	How much?	Where?	Notes

Mindful Moment

You have more time and energy when you're not so consumed by eating. Where will you invest it?

Awareness Journal   Date_____

Time	Why?	When?	What?	How?	How much?	Where?	Notes

Mindful Moment

When you're focused on food (or not eating food), you can't focus on living your life. When you focus on living your life, food becomes the fuel.

Awareness Journal   Date _____

Time	Why?	When?	What?	How?	How much?	Where?	Notes

Mindful Moment

No matter how hard you work on one area of your physical, intellectual, emotional, or spiritual health, it cannot make up for lack in another.

Awareness Journal

Date _____

Time	Why?	When?	What?	How?	How much?	Where?	Notes

Mindful Moment

Mindful movement increases your appreciation of the present moment.

Awareness Journal   Date _____

Time	Why?	When?	What?	How?	How much?	Where?	Notes

Mindful Moment

Practice balance, variety, and moderation in all things.

Am I Hungry?
Mindful Eating Program

Workshop 8
Self-Care Buffer Zone

Awareness Journal   **Date_____**

Time	Why?	When?	What?	How?	How much?	Where?	Notes

Mindful Moment
Don't expect yourself to be perfect.
It isn't possible and it isn't necessary.

©MMXVIII, Am I Hungry?, P.L.L.C.   www.AmIHungry.com

Mindful Eating Program

Awareness Journal

Date _____

Time	Why?	When?	What?	How?	How much?	Where?	Notes

Mindful Moment

You'll finally break free from your eat-repent-repeat cycle when food serves its true purpose: fueling your full and satisfying life.

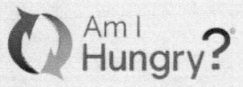

Eat Mindfully, Live Vibrantly

Please visit www.AmIHungry.com

- Find an Am I Hungry? Mindful Eating Program in your area (or start one!).
- Learn about our online Mindful Eating Support Community.
- Join us for a life-changing Am I Hungry? Mindful Eating Retreat.
- Browse our books and workbooks for diabetes, bariatric surgery, binge eating, students, and athletes.
- Download the Am I Hungry? Mindful Eating Virtual Coach app.
- Comment on Dr. May's Eat What You Love blog.
- Read motivational articles and inspiring stories.
- Download free patient education materials.
- Arrange to have Michelle May, M.D. speak at your conference or event.
- Request private Am I Hungry? Mindful Eating Coaching.
- Set up workplace Am I Hungry? workshops or online programs.
- Become a trained and licensed Am I Hungry?® facilitator, therapist, instructor, or coach.
- Purchase this book at special quantity discounts for promotions, fund-raising, book clubs, or educational use.